Total English

ELEMENTARY

Workbook with Key

Mark Foley
and Diane Hall

Contents

1 Your life

LESSON 1.1 (p 4–5)

Vocabulary: countries and nationalities
Pronunciation: word stress
Grammar: *to be*: positive

LESSON 1.2 (p 6–7)

Vocabulary: families
Grammar: possessive *'s*, possessive adjectives, *to be*: questions
Listening: possessions
Reading: countries and nationalities

LESSON 1.3 (p 8–9)

Vocabulary: jobs
Grammar: *a/an; to be*: negative
Pronunciation: /ə/
Reading: jobs

2 Routines

LESSON 2.1 (p 10–11)

Listening and reading: daily routine
Vocabulary: holidays
Grammar: Present Simple *I/you/we*
How to... talk about your daily routine

LESSON 2.2 (p 12–13)

Reading: Julian's day
Vocabulary: verbs
Grammar: Present Simple: *he/she/it/they*, questions
Pronunciation: Present Simple *-s* endings

LESSON 2.3 (p 14–15)

Grammar: noun plurals, *this, that, these, those*
Vocabulary: adjectives (1): colour, opinion
Pronunciation: /ɪ/ and /iː/

3 Activities

LESSON 3.1 (p 16–17)

Grammar: adverbs of frequency
Vocabulary: activities
Reading: activities

LESSON 3.2 (p 18–19)

Vocabulary: sports and games
Reading: Famous families
Grammar: *can/can't*
Pronunciation: /æ/, /ə/, /aː/

LESSON 3.3 (p 20–21)

Reading: Phone facts
Vocabulary: numbers
Pronunciation: word stress
Listening: phone calls and messages
How to... use the phone; take and leave a message

Review and consolidation 1–3 (p 22–23)

4 Food

LESSON 4.1 (p 24–25)

Reading: The story of pizza
Grammar: countable and uncountable nouns
Vocabulary: food
Grammar: *much/many/a lot of*

LESSON 4.2 (p 26–27)

Reading: Recycling facts
Vocabulary: containers, adjectives (2): feelings
Grammar: *a/an, some* and *any*
Pronunciation: /æ/ and /ʌ/

LESSON 4.3 (p 28–29)

Listening: ordering food
How to... order food in a restaurant
Grammar: object pronouns

5 Home

LESSON 5.1 (p 30–31)

Reading: an email
Vocabulary: homes, prepositions of place
Grammar: *there is/there are*
Lifelong learning: Personalise it!

LESSON 5.2 (p 32–33)

Vocabulary: furniture and equipment
Grammar: *have got*
Listening: describing where you live
Pronunciation: /æ/ and /ɒ/

LESSON 5.3 (p 34–35)

Vocabulary: adjectives (3): places
Pronunciation: main stress
Grammar: modifiers (*very, quite, really*)
How to... talk about where you come from/live

6 City life

LESSON 6.1 (p 36–37)

Grammar: Past Simple of *to be*
Reading: a dialogue
Grammar: Past Simple of regular verbs: positive
Pronunciation: Past Simple endings

LESSON 6.2 (p 38–39)

Listening: a short break
Grammar: Past Simple: irregular verbs
Vocabulary: places in a city, shops

LESSON 6.3 (p 40–41)

Reading: Lewis and Clark
Grammar: Past Simple: questions and negatives
Vocabulary: time expressions
Pronunciation: contrastive stress
Reading: Max Van Der Grinten

Review and consolidation 4–6 (p 42–43)

7 People

| LESSON 7.1 | (p 44–45) |

Reading: The wrong note
Lifelong learning: understanding a story
Vocabulary: phrasal verbs
Grammar: articles

| LESSON 7.2 | (p 46–47) |

Reading: a blog
Vocabulary: adjectives (4): people
Lifelong learning: Opposite adjectives
Grammar: pronoun *one/ones*

| LESSON 7.3 | (p 48–49) |

Listening: a summer festival
Vocabulary: ordinal numbers and months
Grammar: possessive pronouns
Pronunciation: /θ/

8 Seasons

| LESSON 8.1 | (p 50–51) |

Listening: a phone call
Grammar: Present Continuous
Pronunciation: sentence stress
How to... describe a picture

| LESSON 8.2 | (p 52–53) |

Reading: Fashions for this autumn
Vocabulary: clothes
Grammar: position of adjectives

| LESSON 8.3 | (p 54–55) |

Vocabulary: the weather
Pronunciation: /ɒ/ and /əʊ/
Reading: Weather wise
Lifelong learning: nouns and adjectives
Grammar: Present Simple and Present Continuous

9 Culture

| LESSON 9.1 | (p 56–57) |

Reading: The future of the book
Vocabulary: news sources
Grammar: comparison of adjectives
Pronunciation: /ə/ in comparatives
How to... give your opinion

| LESSON 9.2 | (p 58–59) |

Vocabulary: films
Grammar: superlative adjectives
Reading: Dan's film choice

| LESSON 9.3 | (p 60–61) |

Listening: tourist information
Grammar: *like/love/hate/prefer*
How to... talk about preferences
Pronunciation: *yes/no* questions

| Review and consolidation 7–9 | (p 62–63) |

10 Journeys

| LESSON 10.1 | (p 64–65) |

Reading: Technology review
Vocabulary: transport
Grammar: *-ing* form as noun
How to... book a train ticket

| LESSON 10.2 | (p 66–67) |

Listening: a job interview
Grammar: Present Perfect with *been*: *I/you/we/they*
Pronunciation: /i/

| LESSON 10.3 | (p 68–69) |

Reading: Mae Jameson
Grammar: Present Perfect: *he/she/it*
Vocabulary: activities
Pronunciation: long and short vowels

11 Learning

| LESSON 11.1 | (p 70–71) |

Reading: Sunshine Holidays
Grammar: *can/can't, have to/don't have to*
Pronunciation: /f/ and /v/

| LESSON 11.2 | (p72–73) |

Reading: an interview
Vocabulary: schools and subjects, new technology
Grammar: review of *wh-* questions
Pronunciation: intonation of *wh-* questions

| LESSON 11.3 | (p 74–75) |

Vocabulary: education
Listening: a phone call
Grammar: the imperative

12 Ambitions

| LESSON 12.1 | (p 76–77) |

Reading: travel and holiday activities
Listening: Planning a trip
Grammar: *be going to*
Pronunciation: sentence stress, /ə/
Vocabulary: future time

| LESSON 12.2 | (p 78–79) |

Reading: Today's news and gossip
Pronunciation: rhymes
Grammar: infinitive of purpose

| LESSON 12.3 | (p 80–81) |

Listening: careers
Grammar: *like* and *would like*
Pronunciation: /aɪ/ and /eɪ/

| Review and consolidation 10–12 | (p 82–83) |

| Key | (p 86–96) |

Vocabulary | countries and nationalities

1 **a** Complete the names of six countries. What is the letter in the centre?

A	U	S	T					A			
	A	R						N	A		
			R					A			
				S				N			
						?					
			B	R							

b Complete the crossword with nationality words.

Across
1 Ronaldo
4 Pope John Paul II
6 Brad Pitt
9 Jaguar cars
10 Mercedes cars
11 Skoda cars

Down
2 Nicole Kidman
3 Toyota cars
5 Javier Bardem
7 Gong Li
8 Leonardo da Vinci
10 Alexander the Great

Pronunciation | word stress

2 ◍ 2 Listen and underline the main stress (the syllable with the strong sound).

Au<u>stra</u>lian
1 Russian
2 German
3 Japanese
4 American
5 Chinese
6 Polish

Grammar | to be: positive

3 Write the full forms.

she's *she is*
1 we're _____
2 I'm _____
3 he's _____
4 they're _____
5 you're _____
6 it's _____

4 Find and <u>underline</u> the mistakes. Then correct them.

He's from Spain. He <u>am</u> Spanish. *is*
1 I'm Clara. I are from Italy. _____
2 We're students. We is Japanese. _____
3 Where be you from? _____
4 It am a mobile phone. _____
5 Brad Pitt – who are he? _____

5 Match the questions with the answers. Then match the answers with the photos.

1 Who is he? ⟍
2 Who is she? ⟍
3 What is it?
4 Who are they?

a a Ferrari sports car ☐
b Vladimir Putin ☒ C
c Alec and William Baldwin ☐
d Claudia Schiffer ☐

7 Complete the questions.

What *is it* ? It's a Nokia phone.

1 Where _____ ? He's from Russia.
2 Where _____ ? They're from Poland.
3 What _____ ? It's a Toyota car.
4 Who _____ ? She's Jennifer López.
5 Where _____ ? I'm from Greece.
6 What _____ ? They're photos.
7 Where _____ ? She's from Portugal.

8 a Read the dialogues and choose the correct words in *italics*.

A: Hello. I'm Maria. I'm Spanish. I'm *of/from* Madrid. (1) *What's/Where's* your name?

B: My name (2) *is/are* Misha. I'm from Warsaw. I'm Polish.

A: Hi, I'm Claudio. I'm (3) *Italy/Italian*. I'm from Rimini.

B: Hi, Claudio. We're (4) *Liz/John and Liz*. We're English. We're from London.

A: Hello, my name is Elda. I'm from São Paulo. I'm Brazilian. (5) *Who's/What's* your name?

B: I'm Jean Pierre. I'm from Montreal. I'm (6) *Canada/Canadian*.

b Now write the names on the map below.

| Claudio | Elda | Jean Pierre | John and Liz |
| Maria | Misha | | |

6 Complete the questions and answers with words from the box.

> Where   is   ~~are~~   German   American
> Russia   from   She's   He's

A: Where *are* Alec and William Baldwin from?
B: They're (1) _____ the United States. They're (2) _____ .
A: Where (3) _____ Vladimir Putin from?
B: (4) _____ from (5) _____ . He's Russian.
A: (6) _____ is Claudia Schiffer from?
B: (7) _____ from Germany. She's (8) _____ .

Vocabulary | families

The Jimenez Family
Cecilia is Eduardo's wife.
Manuel is Eduardo's brother.
Marcela and Juan are Eduardo and Manuel's parents.
Marta is Eduardo and Cecilia's daughter.
Pedro and Alvaro are Eduardo and Cecilia's sons.
Manuel is Marta's uncle.

1 a Read the information about the Jimenez family and complete the family tree.

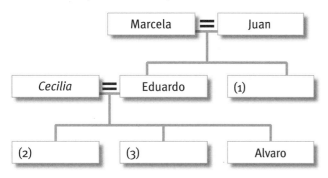

b Complete the sentences.

Marta is Alvaro's *sister* .

1 Alvaro is _____ brother.
2 Cecilia is _____ sister-in-law.
3 Eduardo is Cecilia's _____ .
4 Marta is Manuel's _____ .
5 Marta, Pedro and Alvaro are Cecilia's _____ .
6 Pedro is Eduardo's _____ .
7 Marcela is _____ mother-in-law.
8 Juan is Alvaro's _____ .
9 _____ is Marta's father.

Grammar | possessive 's

2 a Complete the sentences with the words in brackets.

David's watch is Swiss. (David)

1 _____ car is Japanese. (Marianne)
2 _____ computers are American. (Maria)
3 _____ jacket is Italian. (Rafael)
4 _____ wedding ring is beautiful. (Karin)
5 _____ mobile phone is fantastic! (Jane)
6 _____ handbag is blue. (Anna)
7 _____ friend is from Spain. (Paulo)
8 _____ dog is very big. (Connor)
9 _____ sister is twelve. (Nicole)
10 _____ boyfriend is Australian. (Amy)

b Make sentences.

Jack/Hilary/husband
Jack is Hilary's husband.

1 Stefan/Ana/brother

_____

2 Giorgio and Sophia/Mario/parents

_____

3 Clara/Mr and Mrs Moreno/daughter

_____

4 Vanessa/Dieter/sister

_____

5 Alejandro and Elena/Manu/children

_____

6 Victor and Serge/Halyna/sons

_____

7 Stephanie/Pierre/niece

_____

8 José/Isabel/father-in-law

_____

Grammar | possessive adjectives

3 Correct the underlined mistakes. Use possessive adjectives.

Is <u>you</u> sister married? *your*

1 Are <u>he</u> brothers and sisters Canadian? _____
2 Is <u>she</u> house in New York? _____
3 This is <u>I</u> dictionary. _____
4 Jennifer is <u>we</u> cousin. _____
5 Is this <u>you</u> mobile phone? _____

Listening

4 **a** ◉ 3 Listen. Where are the people?

b Cover the audioscript. Listen again and tick (✓) the correct boxes.

Whose is it?	man	woman
bag	✓	✓
1 mobile phone	☐	☐
2 watch	☐	☐
3 jacket	☐	☐
4 wedding ring	☐	☐

c Listen again and label the pictures.

her wedding ring

1 _____

2 _____

3 _____

4 _____

AUDIOSCRIPT

Officer: Excuse me, Sir and Madam. Is this your bag?
Man: Yes.
Woman: Yes, it's our bag.
Officer: Open it, please.
Man: OK.
Officer: Thank you. What about the mobile phone, sir?
Man: It's my wife's.
Officer: And the watch?
Man: It's my watch.
Officer: Is this your jacket, Madam?
Woman: No, it's my husband's.
Officer: And the wedding ring?
Woman: Yes, that's my ring.
Officer: OK. Thank you. You can go now.

Grammar | *to be*: questions

5 Match the questions with the answers.

1 Is Elizabeth your sister? ☐ d
2 Are Sally and John your parents? ☐
3 Is David your brother? ☐
4 Are you a student? ☐
5 Are we in the elementary class? ☐
6 Are Elizabeth and Marie your cousins? ☐

a Yes, I am.
b Yes, we are.
c No, they're my sisters.
d Yes, she is.
e Yes, they are.
f No, he's my boyfriend.

Reading

6 Read the text and answer the questions.

Hi. I'm Amanda. I'm from Melbourne, Australia. I'm Australian, but my parents are from Greece. They're Greek. John is my husband. He's Australian, but his parents are from the United States. Our house is in Sydney. I'm a student at Sydney University.

Is Amanda from Perth?
No, she isn't. She's from Melbourne.

1 Where are Amanda's parents from?
_____

2 What is her husband's name?
_____

3 Is he from the United States?
_____

4 Where are his parents from?
_____

5 Where is John and Amanda's house?
_____

6 Is Amanda a student?
_____

1.3

Vocabulary | jobs

1 Look at the pictures and the letters. Write the job words. Some jobs are two words.

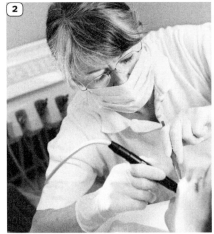

1 REMRFA — _farmer_
2 STIDENT — _____
3 POSH ASSINSATT — _____
_____
4 MOCUTPER GORPAMMRER — _____
_____
5 NINGEREE — _____
6 FECH — _____

2 Find five more jobs in the word chains.

SEAACTCAPORTAIN

TVLAWPRODYERUCER

ARDOCCHITORTECT

sea captain

1 _____   3 _____
2 _____   4 _____
                 5 _____

Grammar | a/an

3 Complete the sentences with *a* or *an*.

Jamie Oliver is _an_ English chef.

1 Stephen Spielberg is ___ famous film director.
2 Hausa is ___ African language.
3 George Clooney is ___ American actor.
4 ___ Ferrari is ___ Italian car.
5 Cristiano Ronaldo is ___ Portuguese footballer.
6 France is ___ European country.

4 Write four sentences about your family and friends. Use the jobs in exercises 1 and 2.

My cousin is a computer programmer.

1 _____
_____
2 _____
_____
3 _____
_____
4 _____
_____

5 Find and underline the mistakes. Then correct them.

My brother is <u>student</u>.   *a student*

Sam's <u>a</u> engineer.   *an engineer*

1 My cousin Julia is an doctor.   _____
2 My grandfather is a retired.   _____
3 Pablo is architect in Brussels.   _____
4 My father is an unemployed.   _____
5 Lucia's friend is lawyer in New York.   _____
6 I'm an chef in my uncle's restaurant.   _____

Pronunciation | /ə/

6 **a** ⬤ 4 Listen to the poem and say the jobs.

An engineer, a farmer, an actor
What job do you do?
An architect, a lawyer, a doctor
What's the job for you?

b Listen again and repeat the whole poem.

Grammar | to be: negative

7 **a** Put the words in the correct order to make sentences.

Luke   married   Susanna   are   and
Luke and Susanna are married.

1 My   20 Cedar Drive   address   is
_____

2 retired   grandparents   are   My
_____

3 young   beautiful   is   cousin   My
_____

4 from   Colombia   's   Esther
_____

5 doctor   's   My   nephew   a
_____

6 Greek   My   are   parents
_____

7 friends   They   're
_____

b Rewrite the sentences from exercise 7a in the negative. Use contracted forms.

Luke and Susanna aren't married.

1 _____
2 _____
3 _____
4 _____
5 _____
6 _____
7 _____

Reading

8 **a** Read the text. <u>Underline</u> six names of people and ⭕circle six jobs.

I'm <u>Michelle</u>. I'm 23 and I'm single. I'm an ⭕actor. My boyfriend is called Martin and he's a police officer. My home is in England, but I'm from France. My parents are in Paris. My father, Daniel, is a lawyer and my mother, Bernadette, is a teacher. My sister Nicole is 27. She's beautiful! She's a model. My brother Francis is a photographer, but he's also a student. My best friend, Heather, is an assistant in a big shop in the centre of London.

b Read the text again. Match the people with their jobs and their relationship to Michelle.

1 Bernadette   a police officer   i   mother
2 Daniel   b teacher   ii   father
3 Francis   c shop assistant   iii best friend
4 Heather   d lawyer   iv   brother
5 Martin   e photographer   v   sister
6 Nicole   f model   vi   boyfriend

9 Read the text again and correct the sentences.

Michelle is married.

No, she isn't married. She's single.

1 Her boyfriend is called Steve.
_____
_____

2 Michelle is English.
_____
_____

3 Her parents are in London.
_____
_____

4 Her mother is a lawyer.
_____
_____

5 Her brother and sister are teachers.
_____
_____

Listening and reading

1 **a** ● 5 Danny is 32. He works at a hotel in the Caribbean. Cover the audioscript. Listen and tick (✓) the correct box.

1   Danny is a holiday rep. ☐
2   Danny is a hotel director. ☐
3   Danny works in the hotel restaurant. ☐

b Listen again and complete the notes about Danny's daily routine.

```
7:30    get up
7:45    have a wash
8:00    (1) _____ with my wife and
        children
9:00    go to the hotel
9:15    (2) _____
9:30    read my emails and faxes
10:30   meet the holiday reps
11:00   (3) _____
12:15   check the hotel rooms and the
        swimming pool
1:00    have lunch in the hotel restaurant
2:15    go to the bank
3:30    meet clients
4:30    write emails and letters
6:30    leave work
7:30    have dinner with my family
10:00   (4) _____
11:30   go to bed
```

AUDIOSCRIPT

Int:	Danny, tell us about your routine.
Danny:	OK. Well, I get up at about half past seven. I have a wash at quarter to eight and then I have breakfast with the family.
Int:	When do you start work?
Danny:	I start work at nine.
Int:	What do you do in the morning?
Danny:	I talk to my assistant and then I read my emails and faxes.
Int:	Do you meet people?
Danny:	Yes, I meet the holiday reps at about half past ten. We have coffee at eleven o'clock in the office and talk about the clients. Then I check the hotel rooms and the swimming pool.
Int:	Do you eat in the hotel?
Danny:	Yes, I do – in the hotel restaurant.
Int:	What do you do after lunch?
Danny:	I go to the bank. Then I meet the hotel clients.
Int:	Do you work in the office?
Danny:	Yes, I write emails and letters.
Int:	When do you go home?
Danny:	I leave work at half past six.
Int:	What do you do in the evening?
Danny:	Well, I have dinner with my wife and children and at ten o'clock I watch TV.

2 **a** You are Danny. Look at the notes in exercise 1b again and answer the questions.

When do you get up?

I get up at half past seven.

1   What do you do at quarter to eight?

_____

2   When do you go to work?

_____

3   What do you do at quarter past twelve?

_____

4   Where do you have lunch?

_____

5   When do you have lunch? ·

_____

6   What do you do in the evening?

_____

7   What do you do at ten o'clock?

_____

8   When do you go to bed?

_____

c Now look at the audioscript and check your answers.

b You are Danny. Write short answers.

Do you have breakfast at half past eight?

No, I don't.

1 Do you have breakfast in a hotel?

_____

2 Are you a hotel director?

_____

3 Do you have a family?

_____

4 Do you have lunch in a restaurant?

_____

5 Do you leave work at six o'clock?

_____

6 Are you 32?

_____

7 Do you go to bed at eleven o'clock?

_____

c Read the questions in exercises 2a and 2b again. Write true answers about you in your notebook.

Vocabulary | holidays

3 Complete the text with words from the box.

> finish   get up   guests   have (x2)
> holiday rep   ~~holidays~~   meet   nightclub
> play   restaurant

❝ We love Fun Club *holidays*. We go every year! We (1) _____ new people and we (2) _____ lots of fun. We (3) _____ late in the mornings and have breakfast in the hotel (4) _____ . We don't talk to the (5) _____ because we don't have any problems! After breakfast we go to the beach or the swimming pool. We (6) _____ lunch there, but we don't eat a lot – just some sandwiches or fruit. After we (7) _____ lunch, we (8) _____ games with the other (9) _____ on the beach. In the evening we go to a (10) _____ . It's fantastic! ❞

Grammar | Present Simple: *I/you/we*

4 Choose the correct words in *italics*.

When do you (start)/ *starts* work?

1 What *do you/do you do* in the evenings?
2 I *not/don't* eat breakfast on Sundays.
3 *Are/Do* you live in a big house?
4 When *you go/do you go* to work?
5 *Do you work/Work you* in a school?
6 When *do you finish/finish you* work?
7 I *do meet/meet* my friends for lunch every day.
8 We don't *go/to go* to nightclubs.

5 Write questions for the answers.

Where do you live?

I live in Sydney, Australia.

1 _____

I work in a hospital.

2 _____

No, I'm not a doctor. I'm a cleaner.

3 _____

I go to work at half past eight.

4 _____

No, I don't have lunch in the hospital.

5 _____

I leave work at half past six.

6 _____

I go to a nightclub with my friends in the evening.

How to... | talk about your daily routine

6 Find five more mistakes and correct them.

A: Do you get up early?   ✓

B: No, I not.   *don't*

A: What do you do in the morning?   1 _____

B: I sleep.   2 _____

A: Get up you at lunch time?   3 _____

B: No, I don't. I get up in the
   evening.   4 _____

A: So, when you go to work?   5 _____

B: At eleven o'clock in the evening. 6 _____

A: And when you do leave work?   7 _____

B: I leave work at eight o'clock in
   the morning.   8 _____

A: Do you work in an office?   9 _____

B: No, don't.   10 _____

A: OK. Do you work in a school?   11 _____

B: Yes, I work. I work in a school at
   night. I'm a cleaner.   12 _____

Reading

1 **a** Read the text quickly and choose the correct words in *italics*.

Julian is a shop *manager/assistant*.

1 He works in *an electrical shop/a bookshop*.

2 He goes to work by *bus/car*.

3 He leaves the shop at *5:15/5:30*.

I'm a shop assistant in a big electrical shop. My day starts at half past six, when I get up and have a wash. I wash my hair, too. Then I have breakfast at quarter past seven and I leave home at quarter to eight. I walk to the bus stop and I wait for the bus. The shop opens at half past eight and I start work. I work in the electrical part of the shop and I sell TVs, DVDs and music systems. I like my job. It's interesting and I talk to a lot of people. I have lunch at half past twelve and I leave work at half past five. I usually play football with friends for about an hour. I have dinner at seven o'clock and I watch TV or listen to CDs in the evening. I go to bed at eleven o'clock.

b Read the text again and complete the table.

6:30	*Julian gets up and has a wash.*
7:15	
7:45	
8:30	
12:30	
5:30	
7:00	
11:00	

Vocabulary | verbs

2 Read the text in exercise 1 again. <u>Underline</u> the present simple verbs. The first two are underlined.

3 **a** Find eight more verbs from the text in the word square and write them below. (→↓↘)

L	I	S	T	E	N	W
S	E	W	Y	A	N	A
R	W	A	S	H	L	L
G	A	T	V	S	F	K
B	I	C	P	E	G	J
Q	T	H	A	V	E	O

listen

1 _____ 5 _____

2 _____ 6 _____

3 _____ 7 _____

4 _____ 8 _____

b Write one verb from the word square before each group of words.

listen to CDs/the radio

1 _____ a wash/lunch/dinner

2 _____ home/work

3 _____ to people/on the phone

4 _____ your hair/your clothes/your car

5 _____ to bed/to work

4 Read the text in exercise 5 and put the pictures in the correct order. Then use words from the box to label the pictures.

> cook dinner   have breakfast   go to bed
> leave home   read a newspaper   ~~wash hair~~

A ☐   B ☐   C [1]   D ☐   E ☐   F ☐

wash hair

_____

_____

_____

_____

_____

Grammar | Present Simple: *he/she/it/they*

5 Complete the text with the correct form of a verb from the box.

> dry   finish   get up   go   have   leave
> listen   make   not/get   not/watch   read
> talk   wash   watch   ~~work~~

Melanie's a hairdresser. She *works* at a film studio. Melanie (1) _____ at about six o'clock in the morning. She has two children and they all (2) _____ breakfast together at seven o'clock. Then Melanie (3) _____ home at half past seven and goes to work. At work she (4) _____ and (5) _____ the actors' hair all day. Her job isn't very interesting, but the actors are nice and they (6) _____ to Melanie about their work.

Sometimes in the afternoon, when Melanie isn't very busy, she (7) _____ the actors at work. Melanie (8) _____ work at half past four, but she (9) _____ home before six. She (10) _____ dinner for her children and then they (11) _____ to bed at about half past eight. In the evening Melanie (12) _____ the newspaper or (13) _____ to music. She (14) _____ films or TV. She goes to bed at about eleven o'clock.

6 Correct the sentences about Melanie.

Melanie works in a shop.

She doesn't work in a shop. She works in a film studio.

1 She leaves home at quarter past eight.

_____

2 She watches the hairdressers in the afternoon.

_____

3 She finishes work at half past six.

_____

4 She makes dinner for her friends.

_____

5 She goes to bed at about ten o'clock.

_____

Grammar | Present Simple: questions

7 **a** Put the words in the correct order to make questions.

day   does   Melanie's   start   What time   ?
What time does Melanie's day start?

1 Where   Melanie   does   work   ?

_____

2 Melanie's children   breakfast   with her   have   Do   ?

_____

3 wash   Does   her children's hair   she   at work   ?

_____

4 Do   talk to   the actors   Melanie   ?

_____

5 she   work   finish   does   When   ?

_____

6 to bed   the children   do   What time   go   ?

_____

7 in the evening   does   Melanie   What   do   ?

_____

8 What time   she   to bed   does   go   ?

_____

b Answer the questions in exercise 7a.

Melanie's day starts at about six o' clock.

1 _____
2 _____
3 _____
4 _____
5 _____
6 _____
7 _____
8 _____

Pronunciation | Present Simple -*s* endings

8 **a** Look at the answers to the questions in exercise 6 and find:

two verbs that end with the /z/ sound, e.g. *listens*.

_____

two verbs that end with the /s/ sound, e.g. *talks*.
works
_____

two verbs that end with the /ɪz/ sound, e.g. *washes*.

_____

b 🔘 6 Listen and check your answers.

Grammar | noun plurals

1 **a** Complete the table. Use a dictionary to check your answers.

	Singular	Plural
	address	*addresses*
1	camera	
2	diary	
3	family	
4	game	
5	holiday	
6	car	
7	scarf	
8	suitcase	
9	watch	
10	wife	

b Complete the sentences. Make the nouns plural and change the verb if necessary.

I have one very good camera.

We *have* two very good *cameras*.

1 She has one holiday a year.

They _____ two _____ a year.

2 He wants to wash the car.

They _____ to wash the _____ .

3 I like my red and green scarf.

We _____ our red and green _____ .

4 Our family works in the shop.

Our two _____ _____ in the shop.

5 Write your address on the form.

Write your _____ on the _____ .

6 I use a desk diary all the time.

We _____ desk _____ all the time.

7 He plays a game of tennis every week.

They _____ three or four _____ of tennis every week.

8 My brother's wife is American.

My brothers' _____ _____ American.

9 I always take one suitcase on holiday.

We always _____ two _____ on holiday.

10 There's a nice watch in that shop.

There _____ a lot of nice _____ in that shop.

Vocabulary | adjectives (1): colour, opinion

2 **a** Write the opposite adjective.

good   *bad*

1 small   _____

2 _____   nice

3 young   _____

4 _____   ugly

5 useful   _____

6 _____   modern

b Now complete the sentences with an adjective from exercise 2a.

A holiday rep is a *good* job.

1 Cuba is a small country, but Canada is _____ .

2 Holidays at the beach are very _____ .

3 My parents aren't _____ . They're only forty-five.

4 Kylie Minogue is very _____ .

5 Mobile phones are _____ .

6 My grandfather's clothes are _____ .

3 Use the clues to complete the puzzle with colours.

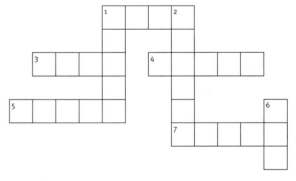

Clues

1 **across** the colour of sharks

2 **down** the colour of taxis in New York

3 **across** water in a swimming pool is this colour

4 **across** men's shoes are often this colour

5 **across** but they're often this colour too

6 **down** Manchester United's colour

7 **across** wedding rings are sometimes this colour

What's the colour in 1 down? _____

Grammar | *this, that, these, those*

4 **a** Match the pictures with the questions.

1 What's this? [C]   3 What are these? ☐
2 What's that? ☐   4 What are those? ☐

A

B

C

D

b Use words from the box to answer the questions in exercise 4a.

> modern   old-fashioned   ~~pretty~~   ugly

1 *This is a pretty scarf.*
2 _____
3 _____
4 _____

5 Complete the dialogue with the questions in exercise 4a.

A: Hello. You have some nice <u>things</u>.
    What's this? <u>It</u>'s very <u>big</u>.
B: The book? It's a <u>dictionary</u>, a <u>Spanish</u> dictionary.
A: Oh, I <u>think</u> my <u>niece</u> wants to study Spanish.
    (1) _____? They're really nice.
B: They're watches.
A: Mm, lovely. (2) _____?
B: That's a bag. It's my old work bag.
A: Mm, it <u>is</u> very old, isn't it? And it's very <u>green</u>,
    too.
B: Yes, but it's very useful.
A: Maybe. And (3) _____?
B: They're belts.
A: Oh, yes, but they're horrible!
B: Do you think so? <u>People</u> usually like them!
A: Oh, do they? I don't, sorry.

Pronunciation | /ɪ/ and /iː/

6 **a** Look at the <u>underlined</u> words in the dialogue in exercise 5. Find words with the same sound.

this (/ɪ/): *things* , It , _____ , _____ ,

_____ , _____ , _____

these (/iː/): _____ , _____ ,

_____

b 🔊 7 Listen and check your answers.

Grammar | adverbs of frequency

Joe, Tracy _____ _____

1 Look at the table and write the names of the people under the pictures.

X = never		✓ = occasionally	✓✓ = sometimes
✓✓✓ = often	✓✓✓✓ = usually		! = always
	Joe	**Lynn**	**Tracy**
cook	!	X	✓
go for a walk	✓	✓✓✓	✓
go on Facebook	✓✓	!	X
go to the cinema	✓✓	✓✓	✓
go to the gym	X	X	✓✓✓✓
listen to music	✓✓✓	X	!
read	!	✓	X
watch a DVD	✓✓✓✓	✓✓	✓

2 **a** Read the text quickly. Then look at the table in exercise 1 again. Who is the text about?

Joe ☐ Lynn ☐ Tracy ☐

❛How do I relax in the evening? Well, I _**often**_ go for a walk after work. I sit at a desk all day and I want to get some exercise. Then I go home and I (1) _____ go on Facebook and read about my friends. I like films, so I (2) _____ go to the cinema and I (3) _____ stay at home and watch a DVD. I (4) _____ read the newspaper or a book. But, you know, I (5) _____ cook! I don't like cooking.❜

b Now complete the text with adverbs of frequency.

3 **a** Look at the table in exercise 1 again. Correct the sentences about Lynn and Tracy.

Tracy never cooks in the evening.

Tracy occasionally cooks in the evening.

1 Tracy often listens to music in the evening.

_____

2 Lynn never watches a DVD in the evening.

_____

3 Lynn always goes to the gym in the evening.

_____

4 Tracy often goes to the cinema in the evening.

_____

5 Tracy sometimes goes to the gym in the evening.

_____

6 Lynn usually goes for a walk in the evening.

_____

b Now look at the information about Joe and write sentences. Use adverbs of frequency.

sometimes/with friends

Joe sometimes goes to the cinema with his friends.

1 never/after work

_____

2 always/in bed

_____

3 usually/in the evening

_____

4 often/after dinner

_____

5 always/at home

_____

6 occasionally/in the park

_____

Vocabulary | activities

4 **a** Complete the table with words from the box.

> a book   a concert   a sandwich
> a walk   an evening class
> my shopping   our homework
> running   the cinema   ~~the gym~~
> the Internet

do	
go for	
go	
go on	
go to	*the gym*
have	
read	

b Complete the sentences with the correct form of a phrase from exercise 4a.

I usually *go to the gym* in the sports centre on Tuesday evenings.

1 Mrs Richards often _____ for lunch on Mondays.

2 We usually _____ when we get home from school. Then we can be ready for school the next day!

3 Jonathan and Karen _____ together at the sports centre on Thursday evening.

4 Tim wants to learn Spanish so he _____ on Wednesday evenings.

5 I always _____ at lunchtime on Friday so I have enough food for the weekend.

6 My grandparents sometimes _____ in the park to get some exercise.

7 My friends all really enjoy music, so we try to _____ every weekend.

8 Lucy and I like good films so we often _____ on Friday evenings.

9 I always _____ for ten minutes in my lunch break to check my emails and read the news.

10 My brother usually _____ in bed. It helps him to relax at the end of the day.

Reading

5 **a** Read the text about Ivan quickly. Which two activities *doesn't* Ivan do?

go for a walk ☐   go to an evening class ☐
go on Facebook ☐   go to the gym ☐
go running ☐   have lunch with friends ☐
go shopping ☐   read a book ☐
go swimming ☐   watch a DVD ☐
go to a concert ☐

I'm Ivan. I live in the south of France. I'm retired, but I have a lot of friends and I do a lot during the week. I go swimming in the morning on Mondays, Wednesdays and Fridays, and I always go for a long walk with friends on the beach on Sundays. After the walk we have lunch – usually a barbecue. On Tuesday and Thursday mornings I go to the gym and on Thursday evenings I usually go to a concert with friends. On Friday evenings I go on Facebook and read about my friends all over the world, (it's Friday evening now). I go shopping on Saturday mornings, then I stay at home and relax – I read a book or watch a DVD.

b Read the text again. Complete Ivan's diary with the correct activities from the list in exercise 5a.

4 Monday			**8 Friday**
a.m.	p.m.	a.m.	p.m.
go swimming	____	____	____

5 Tuesday			**9 Saturday**
a.m.	p.m.	a.m.	p.m.
____	____	____	____

6 Wednesday			**10 Sunday**
a.m.	p.m.	a.m.	p.m.
____	____	____	____

7 Thursday	
a.m.	p.m.
____	____

Vocabulary | sports and games

1 **a** Match the activities with the words.

1	judo	☑	6	chess	☐
2	skiing	☐	7	basketball	☐
3	cycling	☐	8	rowing	☐
4	windsurfing	☐	9	running	☐
5	yoga	☐	10	tennis	☐

b Write the verbs for each activity in exercise 1a. Use *go*, *play* or *do*.

1 *do judo*   6 _____
2 _____   7 _____
3 _____   8 _____
4 _____   9 _____
5 _____   10 _____

2 **a** <u>Underline</u> the odd one out.

	do:	aerobics	judo	<u>rowing</u>
1	go:	skiing	tennis	running
2	play:	dance	chess	tennis
3	do:	basketball	yoga	aerobics
4	go:	skiing	running	yoga
5	play:	basketball	tennis	aerobics

b Find and <u>underline</u> the mistakes. Then correct them.

I <u>do cycling</u> every weekend. *go cycling*

1 We go dance every Friday evening. _____

2 Do you play aerobics? _____

3 We do swimming at the swimming pool. _____

4 My brother does games online every evening. _____

5 They go judo twice a week. _____

Reading

3 **a** Read the text quickly and choose the best title.

1 Famous brothers and sisters ☐
2 Famous fathers and sons ☐
3 Famous families ☐

People say that family members often have the same abilities. Look at these famous examples and you can see that it's true:

- In sport we have the famous footballers, brothers Gary and Phil Neville, and in tennis you can find lots of famous sisters, for example Serena and Venus Williams, and Alona and Kateryna Bondarenko. Michael and Ralf Schumacher are also famous for driving racing cars.

- In show business everyone knows Julia Roberts. Not a lot of people know her brother Eric, but he also acts. Kylie Minogue is a very famous singer, but her sister Danii is also famous for acting and singing. The brothers Joel and Ethan Coen are both famous for the interesting films they make together.

- But it isn't only brothers and sisters. Some fathers and daughters are famous, too. For example, actor Keith Allen and his very famous daughter, Lily Allen, the pop singer.

b Read the text again and match the people with the activities.

1	Serena and Venus Williams	a	act.
2	Julia and Eric Roberts	b	sing.
		c	play tennis.
3	The Neville brothers	d	play football.
4	Michael and Ralf Schumacher	e	drive racing cars.
		f	make good films.
5	The Coen brothers		
6	Kylie and Danii Minogue		

Grammar | *can/can't*

4 Complete the sentences with phrases from exercise 3b. Use *can*.

Serena Williams *can play tennis.*

1 Kylie Minogue _____ .
2 Michael Schumacher _____ .
3 Julia Roberts _____ .
4 Ethan Coen _____ .
5 Gary Neville _____ .

5 **a** Complete the dialogue with *can* or *can't*.

A: Good morning, Miss Randall. Let me ask you a few questions. We have about sixty children here all the time. *Can* you organise games for sixty children?

B: Yes, I (1) _____ . I do that in my job now.

A: Oh, good. And how about your skills? Can you sing?

B: Yes, I (2) _____ sing and dance. I (3) _____ paint, but I can draw.

A: OK. Now sports: we want our organisers to help the children learn sports.

B: Well, I can ride a bike and I (4) _____ play tennis.

A: Good. (5) _____ you teach any other activities, for example, judo?

B: No, not judo, but I (6) _____ teach aerobics.

A: (7) _____ you play the guitar?

B: No, I (8) _____ .

A: Now, we have children from other countries. Can you speak other languages?

B: Yes, I (9) _____ speak German and Spanish.

A: French?

B: No, I (10) _____ speak French.

A: OK. And (11) _____ you drive?

B: Yes, I (12) _____ .

A: Thank you, Miss Randall. That's all for now.

b Look at the dialogue in exercise 5a again. Write sentences about what Miss Randall *can* and *can't* do.

(sing/dance)

She can sing and dance.

(paint/draw)

She can't paint, but she can draw.

1 (ride a bike/play tennis)

_____

_____

2 (teach judo/aerobics)

_____

_____

3 (play/guitar)

_____

_____

4 (speak German/Spanish/French)

_____

_____

5 (drive)

_____

_____

Pronunciation | /æ/, /ə/, /ɑː/

6 8 Listen to the dialogue. Listen for the pronunciation of *can* and *can't*. Tick (✓) the correct column.

	/æ/	/ə/	/ɑː/
Can you organise … ?	☐	✓	☐
1 Yes, I can.	☐	☐	☐
2 Yes, I can sing …	☐	☐	☐
3 I can't paint …	☐	☐	☐
4 … I can play tennis.	☐	☐	☐
5 Can you teach … ?	☐	☐	☐
6 I can teach aerobics.	☐	☐	☐
7 Can you play the guitar?	☐	☐	☐
8 No, I can't.	☐	☐	☐
9 Yes, I can speak German …	☐	☐	☐
10 No, I can't speak French.	☐	☐	☐
11 And can you drive?	☐	☐	☐
12 Yes, I can.	☐	☐	☐

Reading

1 **a** Read the text quickly and match the headings (a–c) with paragraphs 1–3.

a Who makes mobile phones? ☐

b What can mobile phones do? ☐

c Who uses mobile phones? ☐

Phone facts

1 Luxembourg is a small country. It only has 487,751 people. But it has 432,400 mobile phones – 88 percent of the people have phones. That means almost all the people, including small children, have mobiles. China has a lot of people and 55 percent of them have mobile phones – but that's about 738 million phones!

2 Hundreds of companies make mobile phones, but there are only three really big ones. Nokia makes about 35 percent of the world's phones. Samsung makes 20 percent and LG makes about 10 percent.

3 All mobile phones can make phone calls and send text messages. But these days about 22 percent of mobile phones are 'smart phones' – they can use the Internet, send photos and emails and tell you where you are.

b Read the text again and complete the sentences with numbers.

LG makes about _10_ percent of the world's phones.

1 There are _____ mobile phones in Luxembourg.

2 About _____ percent of Chinese people have mobile phones.

3 There are _____ million mobile phones in China.

4 Nokia makes about _____ percent of the world's mobile phones.

5 About _____ percent of mobile phones are 'smart phones'.

Vocabulary | numbers

2 Complete the table with the numbers from the text in exercise 1a. Write them as numbers and words.

	487, 751	four hundred and eighty seven thousand, seven hundred and fifty-one
1		
2		
3		
4		
5		
6		
7		
8		

3 Answer the questions. Write numbers and words.

How old is your teacher?

34 (thirty-four)

1 How old are you?

_____

2 How many students are there in your class?

_____

3 How many people live in your town/city?

_____

4 How many people live in your country?

_____

5 How many pages are there in this book?

_____

Pronunciation | word stress

4 **a** 🔊 9 Listen and <u>underline</u> the main stress.

four<u>teen</u>　　　3 fifty

1 forty　　　4 eighty

2 fifteen　　　5 eighteen

b 🔘 10 Listen and tick (✓) the sentences you hear.

	a	I'm fifteen years old.	☐
	b	I'm fifty years old.	✓
1	a	That's $18.90.	☐
	b	That's $80.19.	☐
2	a	Our address is 17 Grove Road.	☐
	b	Our address is 70 Grove Road.	☐
3	a	It costs €14.40.	☐
	b	It costs €40.14.	☐
4	a	We have sixteen DVDs.	☐
	b	We have sixty DVDs.	☐

Listening

5 **a** 🔘 11 Cover the audioscript. Listen to three phone calls and number them 1–3.

a message on an answerphone ☐
a phone call to an office ☐
a voicemail message ☐

b Listen again and complete the messages.

1
Caller: _____Lucy_____
Phone number: _____
Message:
call her this afternoon after 2:20

2
Caller: _____Fiona_____
Phone number: _____
Message:
She can't _____

3
Caller: __Dr Gupta__
Phone number: _____
Message:
_____

How to... | use the phone; take and leave a message

6 **a** Cover the audioscript. Complete the dialogue.

A: Hello. Davis and Davis.

B: *Good afternoon.* Can *I speak to* Michael Jenkins?

A: I'm afraid he's not here today. Can I (1) _____ a message?

B: Yes. Can you (2) _____ him to phone Dr Gupta?

A: Of course. What's your (3) _____ ?

B: It's 894 7701.

A: Dr Gupta, 894 7701. Anything else?

B: Yes, can you ask him to (4) _____ after half past four?

A: Of course.

B: Thanks. Bye.

A: Goodbye.

b 🔘 12 Listen and check your answers.

AUDIOSCRIPT

1

A: Thank you for calling your Tel-call voicemail service. You have one message.

B: Hi Daniel, it's Lucy. Can you call me this afternoon after twenty past two? My number's 09404 8832. Thanks.

2

A: This is Phil and Isabel's phone. We're not here at the moment, so please leave a message with your name and number after the tone.

B: Phil? It's Fiona. I can't see you tomorrow because there's an important meeting at my office. How about ten past seven on Friday? You can call me on 0991 344562.

3

A: Hello. Davis and Davis.

B: Good afternoon. Can I speak to Michael Jenkins?

A: I'm afraid he's not here today. Can I take a message?

B: Yes. Can you ask him to phone Dr Gupta?

A: Of course. What's your number?

B: It's 894 7701.

A: Dr Gupta, 894 7701. Anything else?

B: Yes, can you ask him to call after half past four?

A: Of course.

B: Thanks. Bye.

A: Goodbye.

7 Find five more mistakes and correct them.

A: Hello.

B: Hello. Can I speak <u>of</u> Clare Higgins?   <u>to</u>

A: I'm afraid she isn't there today. Can I make a message?   1 _____
2 _____

B: Yes. Can you speak her to call Erik Langley at the bank?   3 _____

A: Of course. What are your number?   4 _____

B: I am 02099543301.   5 _____

A: OK. Goodbye.

B: Bye.

Grammar
Subject pronouns

1 Complete the sentences with subject pronouns.

My brother works in an office in London. _He_'s a computer programmer.

1 Our mother is a very good cook. _____ cooks French and Italian food.
2 My friends and I love tennis. _____ play it every week.
3 My uncle and aunt live in Canada. _____ have an apartment in Vancouver.
4 Three of us are at school together. My sisters are in Year 4, but _____'m in Year 5.
5 I go to aerobics once a week. _____'s good fun.
6 The new _Star Trek_ film is on at the cinema. Do _____ want to come and see it with me?

to be

2 **a** Complete the questions and answers with the correct form of _to be_.

1 Where _is_ she from?
2 How old _____ you?
3 What _____ it?
4 Who _____ he?
5 _____ you married?
6 _____ she a student?
7 _____ he Russian?
8 _____ they from Chile?
9 Where _____ São Paulo?
10 What _____ they?

a No, he _____ .
b No, I _____ not.
c It _____ a mobile phone.
d Yes, she _____ .
e He _____ Barack Obama.
f No, they _____ .
g They _____ mobile phones.
h It _____ in Brazil.
i I _____ nineteen.
j She _____ from Poland.

b Look at exercise 2a again and match the questions with the answers.

Possessive 's and possessive adjectives

3 Choose the correct words in _italics_.

Is David _you_/_your_ son?

1 'Excuse me, are you _Marias'_/_Maria's_ cousin?' 'No, I'm _his_/_her_ husband.'
2 Is Elizabeth _their_/_their's_ grandmother?
3 I'm from England and _my_/_our_ wife is from Scotland.
4 Greg's a lawyer but _his_/_their_ sons are actors.
5 We're Canadian but _my_/_our_ parents are from Turkey.
6 Is this _Williams_/_William's_ coat?
7 My sister and I live with _we_/_our_ grandfather.
8 Do you like _me_/_my_ new MP3 player?

Present Simple and adverbs of frequency

4 Complete the sentences with the correct form of the verb in brackets. Put the adverb in the correct place.

Julia _often watches_ television in the evening. (often/watch)

What time _do you usually start_ work in the morning? (you/usually/start)

1 My sister _____ in a restaurant. (sometimes/work)
2 David _____ to work. (never/walk)
3 Where _____ lunch? (John/usually/have)
4 Mrs Dawson _____ swimming. (occasionally/go)
5 _____ her car on Saturday morning? (Susan/always/wash)
6 The children _____ to school at the weekend. (not/go)
7 My mother _____ in the city. (not/live)
8 We _____ very busy in this shop. (often/be)

Present simple and a/an

5 Complete the phrases with _a_ or _an_. Then make questions.

she/live/in _a_ big city?

Does she live in a big city?

1 he/often/stay/in __ hotel?

_____

2 you/have/__ break at lunchtime?

_____

3 your parents/have/__ holiday every year?

_____

4 you/work/in __ office?

_____

5 he/be/__ student?

_____

6 they/have/__ unemployed son?

_____

7 she/work/in __ famous restaurant?

_____

8 you/have/__ iPod?

_____

this, that, these, those

6 Choose the correct answer.

_B_ is my new watch. Do you like it?

A These   **B** This   C Those

1 Look at the shop window over there. Isn't ___ a beautiful coat?

  A this   **B** those   C that

2 Go to your room and put all ___ books away now!

  A those   **B** these   C this

3 Look! ___ is the new James Bond DVD. It's really exciting.

  A Those   **B** This   C These

4 Oh yuk! ___ sandwiches are horrible!

  A This   **B** That   C These

Noun plurals

7 Write the plural form of the nouns in the correct column. There are two nouns in each column.

	Add -s	Add -es	Remove -f, add -ves	Remove -y, add -ies	Irregular
address book child city diary wife man game scarf watch	_books_	_addresses_			

can/can't

8 Make questions and answers with _can/can't_.

you/play tennis? (✓)

A: _Can you play tennis?_

B: _Yes, I can._

Darius/speak French? (✗)

A: _Can Darius speak French?_

B: _No, he can't._

1 you/sing? (✓)

  A: _____

  B: _____

2 your husband/cook? (✗)

  A: _____

  B: _____

3 she/speak Spanish and Portuguese? (✓)

  A: _____

  B: _____

4 you/do judo? (✓)

  A: _____

  B: _____

5 a DVD player/send emails? (✗)

  A: _____

  B: _____

Vocabulary

9 **a** Tick (✓) the correct box.

	job	family	verb	adjective
doctor	✓	☐	☐	☐
1 daughters	☐	☐	☐	☐
2 leave	☐	☐	☐	☐
3 invent	☐	☐	☐	☐
4 get up	☐	☐	☐	☐
5 chef	☐	☐	☐	☐
6 play	☐	☐	☐	☐
7 horrible	☐	☐	☐	☐
8 uncle	☐	☐	☐	☐
9 pretty	☐	☐	☐	☐

b Complete the sentences with words from exercise 9a.

Amy works in a restaurant. She is a _chef_.

1 I'm a _____ . I work in a hospital.

2 My father's brother is my _____ .

3 We have two _____ , Kim and Jo.

4 Jane and Mary are very _____ girls.

5 We _____ work at six o'clock.

6 What time do you _____ in the morning?

7 I want to work in a theme park and _____ new rides.

8 We sometimes _____ tennis on Wednesday afternoon.

9 Don't buy that coat. It's _____ !

10 Match the activities with the places.

1	see a film	a	gym
2	dance	b	concert hall
3	sunbathe	c	cinema
4	buy things	d	beach
5	go for a walk	e	restaurant
6	have dinner	f	school
7	listen to live music	g	home
8	do aerobics	h	park
9	watch TV	i	shop
10	learn English	j	nightclub

4 Food

Reading

1 **a** Read the text quickly and choose the best title.

1 How to cook pizza ☐
2 The story of pizza ☐
3 Pizza in the USA ☐

Millions of people love <u>pizzas</u>. There are so many different types! Most pizzas have tomatoes and cheese, but there are more than a hundred other things you can put on a pizza! Some people like them with beef or chicken, some with seafood, others like pineapple on their pizzas! Which type do you like?

People like pizzas because they come in many different sizes. You can get a big pizza or buy a small piece if you are not very hungry. You can eat them in a normal restaurant or a special pizza restaurant (a pizzeria), you can eat them in the street, or you can phone a takeaway and they bring a hot pizza to your house in a box. There are thousands and thousands of pizza restaurants all over the world. In the US there are more than 100,000! But where does pizza come from?

Well, the original pizza restaurant is in Naples, Italy. Its name is Antica Pizzeria Port' Alba. It is 200 years old and, of course, they cook their pizzas the old Italian way. It's still open and you can go in there today and enjoy a fantastic pizza.

b Read the text again and complete the questions and answers.

A: *What* do most pizzas have?
B: Most pizzas have (1) _____ .
A: (2) _____ a pizzeria?
B: It's (3) _____ restaurant.
A: How many pizza (4) _____ has the US got?
B: The US has got (5) _____ .
A: Where is the (6) _____ restaurant?
B: It's in (7) _____ .

Grammar | countable and uncountable nouns

2 **a** <u>Underline</u> all the food words in the text. Then write them in the table.

Countable	Uncountable
pizzas	

b Now write the words from the box in the table above.

banana beans bread burger hotdog
potato rice tea water

3 Choose the correct words in *italics*.

I drink (a lot of)/*many* milk every day.
1 Milk *isn't*/*aren't* expensive.
2 I don't drink *much*/*many* orange juice.
3 How *much*/*many* burgers are there?
4 Potatoes *is*/*are* easy to cook.
5 People say sugar *is*/*are* bad for you.
6 Do English people drink *a lot of*/*many* tea?
7 How *much*/*many* bread do you want?
8 I think mineral water *is*/*are* very boring.
9 Do you drink *a lot of*/*many* water?
10 How *much*/*many* apples have you got?

Vocabulary | food

4 **a** Find and circle eight more food and drink words in the word chain. Then write them below.

lamb

1 _____   5 _____
2 _____   6 _____
3 _____   7 _____
4 _____   8 _____

b Use words from exercise 4a to write labels for the pictures.

A eggs

Grammar | *much/many/a lot of*

5 Match 1–6 with a–f.

1 How many   a of rice.
2 How much   b bananas do you eat?
3 Do you drink a lot of   c burgers.
4 I don't eat many   d tea?
5 She doesn't eat   e coffee do you drink?
6 I usually buy a lot   f much seafood.

6 Write questions with *How much* or *How many*. Then write answers that are true for you.

apples/you/eat/every week?

How many apples do you eat every week?

I eat three apples every week.

1 rice/you/buy/at the supermarket?

_____

_____

2 water/you/drink/every day?

_____

_____

3 oranges/you/buy/at the market?

_____

_____

4 bananas/your family/eat/every week?

_____

_____

5 coffee/you/drink/at the weekend?

_____

_____

6 burgers/you/eat/every week?

_____

_____

7 **a** Read the information about Ana and Karim and decide if these statements are true (T) or false (F).

Ana eats a lot of pork.   F

1 She doesn't eat many potatoes.   ☐
2 She doesn't eat a lot of fish.   ☐
3 Karim eats a lot of beef and lamb.   ☐
4 He doesn't eat much fruit.   ☐
5 He doesn't eat many vegetables.   ☐

Ana likes fruit, rice, pasta and seafood. She doesn't like meat or vegetables.

Karim likes meat and vegetables. He doesn't like fish, apples or bananas.

b Who likes these things? Write *A* for Ana or *K* for Karim.

carrots   K   4 hot dogs ☐
1 watermelons ☐   5 bananas ☐
2 pineapple ☐   6 burgers ☐
3 chicken ☐   7 potatoes ☐

Reading

Recycling facts

Every week we put a lot of rubbish in our bins, but is this necessary? We can recycle lots of things and use them to make other, different things. So how green are we in the UK? Here are some surprising facts about rubbish and recycling:

1 People in the UK recycle about 40 percent of their rubbish every year.

2 We can recycle about 60 percent of the rubbish in our bins: we can recycle all glass bottles and jars, paper bags, boxes and packets. We can't usually recycle plastic bags or juice cartons.

3 A family in the UK uses about 500 glass bottles and jars every year.

4 We can use glass again and again and again!

5 A recycled can is part of a new can in six weeks!

6 We read and recycle about 38 kg of newspapers every year.

7 We can even recycle our old mobile phones.

So do you recycle? Start recycling and go green!

1 **a** Read the text quickly. Where can you see this kind of text?

1 in a book ☐
2 in a magazine ☐
3 on a carton ☐

b Read the text again. Which fact answers each question? Write the number.

How many newspapers do we read every year? _6_

1 Can we recycle fruit juice cartons? _____
2 Is glass useful? _____
3 How much rubbish do people in the UK recycle every year? _____
4 Can we recycle other things, i.e. not bottles, jars or other containers? _____
5 How many glass bottles and jars do we use every year? _____
6 Can we recycle plastic bags? _____

Vocabulary | containers

2 Use container words to write labels for the picture.

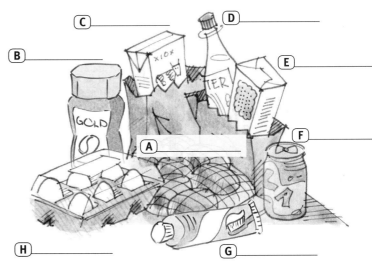

3 a Put the letters in the correct order to write container words.

N A C *can*

1 T O T L E B _____
2 O X B _____
3 C O R A N T _____
4 B U T E _____
5 T E K C A P _____
6 G A B _____
7 A R J _____

b Complete the phrases with container words.

a *bag* of rice/potatoes

1 a _____ of coffee/maple syrup
2 a _____ of water/milk
3 a _____ of eggs/chocolates
4 a _____ of cola/tomatoes
5 a _____ of fruit juice/milk
6 a _____ of toothpaste/tomato paste
7 a _____ of biscuits/crisps

Grammar | *a/an*, *some* and *any*

4 Write the list of ingredients for lamb and potato bake. Use *a* or *some* and a word from the box.

can of tomatoes   ~~carrots~~   dried fruit
lamb   nuts   potato (1)   salt

1 *some carrots*   5 _____
2 _____   6 _____
3 _____   7 _____
4 _____

5 Complete the dialogue with *a/an*, *some* or *any* and the correct form of the words in brackets.

A: Let's write our shopping list for the supermarket.

B: OK. I think we need *some mineral water* (mineral water).

A: No, we don't need (1) _____ (mineral water). We have six bottles. We have (2) _____ (lamb) and (3) _____ (dried fruit). Why don't we have a lamb and potato bake tonight?

B: OK. Do we have (4) _____ (potato)?

A: No, we don't. Can you get some? Oh, get (5) _____ (chocolate) for my mother, too. A nice big box, please. Do you have (6) _____ (money)?

B: Well, I don't have (7) _____ (cash), but I have (8) _____ (credit card).

A: OK. Do you want a cup of coffee before you go?

B: Yes, please! And can I have (9) _____ (biscuit), too? Just one!

A: No, we don't have (10) _____ (biscuit). Put biscuits on the shopping list!

Pronunciation | /æ/ and /ʌ/

6 a Underline the syllables with /æ/ (*pasta*) and /ʌ/ (*some*) in these words. Then write the words in the table.

~~businessman~~   carrot   grandparents   hungry
laptop   money   nightclub   package   programme
sunbathe   Sunday   unemployed

/æ/	/ʌ/
business*man*	

b 🔵 13 Listen and check your answers.

Vocabulary | adjectives (2): feelings

7 Match the adjectives with the descriptions.

1 hungry
2 healthy
3 fit
4 tired
5 thirsty
6 unhealthy

a You feel this when you want to sleep.
b You are this when you eat and drink the wrong things.
c You feel this when you want to eat.
d You feel this when you want to drink.
e You are this when you eat and drink the right things.
f You are this when your body is in good condition.

Super Pizza

Free delivery!

PIZZAS	small	large
cheese and tomato	€5.95	€6.95
beef and tomato	€8.25	(1) _____
seafood and pineapple	€7.50	€8.50
vegetarian	€7.25	€9.95

SIDE ORDERS		
fries	€2.25	€3.35
tomato salad	€2.45	(2) _____
seafood salad	€3.00	€3.99

DRINKS		
mineral water	€1.25	€2.15
coffee	(3) _____	(4) _____
cola	€1.95	€2.35
orange juice	€3.25	€3.95

Call 09909700700 to order.
We accept all major credit cards or you can pay cash on delivery.

AUDIOSCRIPT

Super Pizza: Hello, Super Pizza.

Marisa: Hi. How much is a large beef and tomato pizza, please?

Super Pizza: That's eight euros ninety-five.

Marisa: OK. Do you have a seafood and pineapple pizza?

Super Pizza: Yes.

Marisa: How much is a large one?

Super Pizza: Eight euros fifty.

Marisa: Fine. I'd like a large seafood and pineapple pizza.

Super Pizza: Any side orders?

Marisa: How much is a small tomato salad?

Super Pizza: Two euros forty-five. And a large tomato salad is three euros.

Marisa: A small tomato salad, please. What about coffee?

Super Pizza: A small cup of coffee is two euros and a large coffee is two euros seventy-five.

Marisa: A small coffee, please.

Super Pizza: Right. A large seafood and pineapple pizza, a small tomato salad and a small cup of coffee.

Marisa: How much is that?

Super Pizza: That's twelve euros ninety-five.

Marisa: Can I pay by credit card?

Super Pizza: Yes, of course.

Listening

1 **a** 🔘 14 Cover the audioscript. Listen to the phone call and answer the questions.

1 Does Marisa order a pizza?

_____

2 Does she order a drink?

_____

3 How does Marisa pay for the food?

_____

b Listen again. What exactly does Marisa order? How much does it cost? Complete the notes.

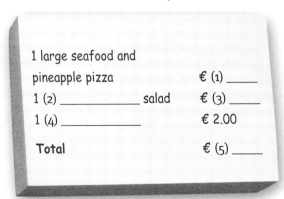

1 large seafood and
pineapple pizza   € (1) _____
1 (2) _____ salad   € (3) _____
1 (4) _____   € 2.00

Total   € (5) _____

c Listen again and complete the prices on the menu at the top of the page.

2 **a** Look at the menu and write questions for the answers.

How much is a small cheese and tomato pizza?
It's €5.95.

1 _____
It's €8.50.

2 _____
It's €3.00.

3 _____
It's €8.25.

b Look at the menu again and match the questions with the answers.

1 Do you have pizzas?   a Yes, I'd like a
2 Can I pay by credit   mineral water.
   card?   b No, we don't.
3 How much is a large   c Yes, you can.
   coffee?   d It's €2.75.
4 Do you have burgers?   e Yes, large fries,
5 Anything to drink?   please.
6 Any side orders?   f Yes, we do.

How to... | order food in a restaurant

3 Choose the correct words in *italics*.

A: Hello, what can I get you today?

B: I'd *want*/*like* a burger, please.

A: Small or large?

B: How (1) *much*/*many* is the large burger?

A: It's €6.95.

B: OK, large, please.

A: Right. A large burger. Any side orders?

B: (2) *Are*/*Do* you have fries?

A: No, we don't. Do you (3) *want*/*like* a salad?

B: OK. A small egg salad.

A: Anything to (4) *eat*/*drink*?

B: Yes, (5) *I'll*/*I'd* have a large cola, please.

A: OK.

B: How much (6) *is*/*are* that?

A: That's €13.35.

B: Can I pay (7) *by*/*of* credit card?

Grammar | object pronouns

4 **a** You are Janine. You are in a restaurant with some friends. Read the notes and write labels for the pictures. Use object pronouns.

Lunch order

Janine: burger and fries

Janine, Steve and Lucy: 3 cups of coffee

Peter: a burger

Alicia: a cheese sandwich and a bottle of mineral water

Linda and Erik: 2 small vegetarian pizzas

 for *me*

 1 for _____

 3 for _____

 2 for _____

 4 for _____

b You are Janine. The waitress asks you about your order. Replace the words in brackets with an object pronoun. Then complete the answers.

Are the two small pizzas for (Alicia) *her*?
No, *they're for them.*

1 Are the fries for (Linda and Erik) _____ ?
No, _____ .

2 Are the three cups of coffee for (Peter) _____ ?
No, _____ .

3 Is the sandwich for (Janine, Steve and Lucy) _____ ?
No, _____ .

4 Is the burger for (Alicia) _____ ?
No, _____ .

5 Is the bottle of mineral water for (Linda and Erik) _____ ?
No, _____ .

5 Rewrite the sentences. Replace the underlined expressions with pronouns.

<u>Our grandmother and grandfather</u> live with <u>my brothers and me</u>.

They live with us.

1 <u>Danny</u> loves <u>Isabel</u>.

_____

2 <u>My boyfriend and I</u> don't like <u>meat</u>.

_____

3 <u>Our teachers</u> help <u>my classmates and me</u> with <u>our homework</u>.

_____

4 <u>My parents</u> visit <u>my grandparents</u> every Saturday afternoon.

_____

5 <u>My brothers and I</u> play football with <u>John</u>.

_____

6 <u>Mrs Field</u> uses <u>her computer</u> every day.

_____

7 Do <u>you and your friends</u> want to have lunch with <u>my friends and me</u>?

_____

8 Does <u>your brother</u> want to take a photo with <u>my mobile phone</u>?

_____

9 Can <u>my sister and I</u> stay with <u>you and your friends</u>?

_____

10 Does <u>your grandfather</u> know how to use <u>the computer</u>?

_____

Reading

1 a Read the text quickly. What kind of text is it?

1 an advert about an apartment for sale ☐
2 an email from one friend to another ☐
3 an email to someone who wants to buy an apartment ☐

From:	Jade
To:	Danny
Att:	apartment 001.jpg

Hi Danny

This is just a short email with a photo of my new <u>apartment</u>. It's in a really unusual building. The apartments are quite small and outside they are all different colours with very big windows.

My apartment has air conditioning, so it's cool inside when it's hot outside. It's very small – there's a living room, but there isn't a dining room. The kitchen is next to the living room, but it's very small – I don't want to cook a lot anyway! It has one bedroom and a shower room, but it's OK for one person. It doesn't have a garden or a patio, but I love it.

The school is great and the other teachers are all nice. Japan's an interesting country. I want to see a lot of it in the next few weeks.

b Read the text again. Which photo (1–2) and floor plan (A–B) does it describe?

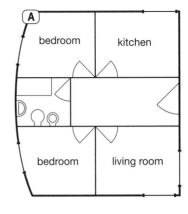

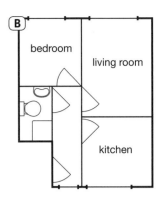

c Read the text again and decide if these statements are true (T) or false (F).

There is a photo with the email. [T]

1 Jade lives in an unusual apartment block. ☐
2 She has a large apartment. ☐
3 Her apartment has a dining room. ☐
4 She doesn't want to live there. ☐
5 She is a teacher in a school. ☐

Vocabulary | homes

2 a <u>Underline</u> these words in the text. The first one is underlined.

1 one word for a type of home
2 five words for rooms
3 four words for other parts/features of a home

b Use the words from exercise 2a to complete the word map. Then add the words and phrases from the box.

> attic   bathroom   cellar   central heating
> detached house   double glazing   garage
> solar panels   study   terrace
> terraced house   villa

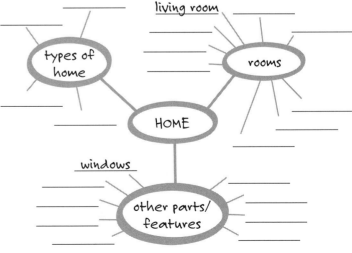

Grammar | *there is/there are*

3 Complete the sentences with the correct form of *there is/there are*. Use contracted forms.

There's a famous zoo in Berlin.

1 _____ some interesting things to do in our town.

2 _____ any shops near here?

3 _____ a good Chinese takeaway in the centre of the city.

4 _____ a garage with the house, but there's space outside for two cars.

5 _____ a gym near here?

6 _____ a garden with the apartment, but there is a large terrace.

7 _____ any detached houses in this part of the town, only terraced houses.

8 _____ a message for Christine on the voicemail.

9 _____ a concert in the concert hall this Saturday?

10 _____ two bathrooms in the house?

4 Look at floor plan A and complete the text with the correct form of *there is/there are* or the names of rooms.

Hi Anna

The university here in Germany is great! I have a lovely apartment in a very unusual building in Darmstadt. *There are* a lot of apartments in the building and (1) _____ a nice roof garden. (2) _____ also a garage for cars under the building. Oh, and (3) _____ a café in the building too! That's really good! But (4) _____ any shops – I go into town for the shops.

My apartment is quite big: there are two big (5) _____ and there's a (6) _____ between the bedrooms. (7) _____ a living room with a big (8) _____ opposite it, but (9) _____ a dining room. (10) _____ very good central heating, but (11) _____ any air conditioning. But we don't need that here – it's usually quite cold!

Love
Heather

Lifelong learning | Personalise it!

5 Write sentences about your home. Use the words in brackets.

(CD player) *There's a CD player in my bedroom.*

(bathroom) *There are two bathrooms in my apartment.*

1 (television) _____

_____

2 (bedrooms) _____

_____

3 (garage) _____

_____

4 (cellar) _____

_____

5 (dining room) _____

_____

6 (central heating) _____

_____

7 (garden) _____

_____

8 (study) _____

_____

9 (attic) _____

_____

10 (solar panels) _____

_____

Vocabulary | prepositions of place

6 Correct the underlined prepositions. Sometimes more than one preposition is possible.

I'd like to have a villa <u>in</u> the sea. *near/next to*

1 There's a cellar <u>on</u> our house. _____

2 Our apartment has a roof garden <u>under</u> it. _____

3 My hotel room is next to your room and we share the bathroom <u>behind</u> our rooms. _____

4 We have a small library <u>on</u> our living room. _____

5 My grandparents have a house in the country with a large garden <u>in</u> it. _____

6 There are two solar panels <u>in</u> the roof of the eco-villa. _____

7 We're neighbours – their house is right <u>between</u> ours. _____

8 The school is <u>under</u> our house – it only takes me five minutes to walk there. _____

Vocabulary | furniture and equipment

1 **a** Match 1–6 with a–f. Then write the furniture and equipment below.

1	washing	a	board
2	music	b	machine
3	micro	c	washer
4	cup	d	wave
5	dish	e	table
6	dining	f	system

1 *washing machine*

2 _____

3 _____

4 _____

5 _____

6 _____

b Use words from exercise 1a to write labels for the pictures.

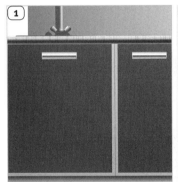

cupboard _____   _____

_____   _____

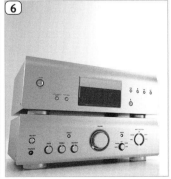

_____   _____

2 Match the words and phrases in the box with the descriptions.

> bed   chair   coffee table   ~~cooker~~   desk
> fridge   lamp   sofa   TV

You can cook meals on it. *cooker*

1 You can put drinks on it. _____

2 Two or three people can sit on it. _____

3 You can watch it. _____

4 You can put milk in it. _____

5 You can do your homework on it. _____

6 You can sleep in it. _____

7 Only one person can sit on it. _____

8 This gives you light when it's dark. _____

Grammar | have got

3 Write sentences with *have/has got*. Use contracted forms.

Jenny/an apartment in the city

Jenny's got an apartment in the city.

1 I/two brothers

_____

2 they/a swimming pool

_____

3 Álvaro/a laptop computer

_____

4 we/a new sofa

_____

5 you/a phone message

_____

6 I/three children

_____

4 Write questions (?) or negative sentences (✗). Use contracted forms in the negative sentences.

I've got a car. (✗)

I haven't got a car.

Maria's got a dictionary. (?)

Has Maria got a dictionary?

1 We've got a big kitchen. (✗)

_____

2 Your girlfriend's got a good job. (?)

_____

3 She's got a mobile phone. (✗)

_____

4 They've got a microwave. (?)

_____

5 He's got a credit card. (✗)

_____

5 Write questions with *have/has got*. Then write short answers that are true for you.

your town/theatre?

Has your town got a theatre?

Yes, it has.

1 your town/a shopping centre?

_____
_____

2 your town/an airport?

_____
_____

3 you/any children?

_____
_____

4 you/any brothers or sisters?

_____
_____

6 Write three sentences about you and your family with *have got* and *but*. Use the furniture and equipment in exercises 1 and 2.

I've got a cooker, but I haven't got a microwave.

My sister's got a washing machine, but she hasn't got a dishwasher.

1 _____
_____

2 _____
_____

3 _____
_____

Listening

7 **a** 🔵 15 Cover the audioscript. Listen to Serena. Where does she live? Listen and tick (✓) the correct picture.

b Listen again and complete the sentences with *have/has got* and a number.

Their house *has got four* bedrooms.

1 Serena and Harry _____ children.
2 Serena _____ cats.
3 Harry _____ computers.
4 They _____ DVDs.

c Listen again and answer the questions. Write short answers.

Has Serena got an apartment in the city?

No, she hasn't.

1 Have Serena and Harry got any children?

_____

2 Has Serena got a car?

_____

3 Has her husband got a car?

_____

4 Has Serena's house got a terrace?

_____

5 Have they got a dining room?

_____

6 Have they got a TV?

_____

AUDIOSCRIPT

I live in a big house in the country with my husband, Harry. The house has got four bedrooms and a big garden. We've got two children and three cats. They love the garden. They play in it every day. And we've got a garage. I haven't got a car, but my husband has. I'm an artist and I work at home. I use one of the bedrooms. It's got a big terrace. I can sit on the terrace in the summer and paint the garden – it's lovely. Harry's got three computers. Actually, he's got lots of electronic things in the house. He's got a digital camera and he makes DVDs. In fact, we've got forty DVDs now. In the evenings we eat dinner in the kitchen – we haven't got a dining room. Then we watch TV in the living room.

Pronunciation | /æ/ and /ɒ/

8 🔵 16 Listen to the underlined sounds in these words and tick (✓) the correct column.

	/æ/	/ɒ/
g<u>o</u>t	☐	✓
c<u>a</u>t	✓	☐
1 h<u>o</u>spital	☐	☐
2 p<u>o</u>cket	☐	☐
3 t<u>a</u>p	☐	☐
4 sh<u>o</u>p	☐	☐
5 p<u>a</u>cket	☐	☐
6 h<u>o</u>t	☐	☐

Vocabulary | adjectives (3): places

1 **a** Complete the crossword with adjectives and places. Then answer the question below.

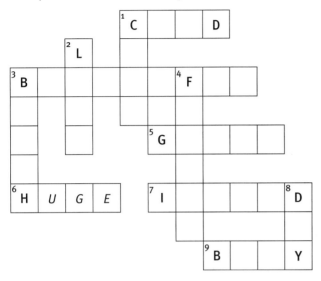

Clues

❯ New York is a _____ – millions of people live there. [6 across] [1 down]

❯ There's a _____ in my country – there isn't any water in it. [8 down] [2 down]

❯ The New Forest is a _____ in the south of England. [3 across] [4 down]

❯ Kefalonia is a very _____ – it has a lot of trees. [5 across] [7 across]

❯ Copacabana in Rio de Janeiro is a very _____ – a lot of people go there. [9 across] [3 down]

One adjective from the crossword isn't in the clues. Which adjective? _____

b Cross out the adjective that we do not use to describe each place.

	river:	dangerous	~~modern~~	wide
1	desert:	hot	dry	wet
2	mountain:	friendly	high	cold
3	city:	dry	noisy	busy
4	beach:	popular	huge	high
5	island:	green	low	tropical
6	forest:	old	busy	beautiful
7	lake:	green	dry	small
8	hill:	low	hot	pretty
9	country:	beautiful	high	huge
10	river:	wide	long	green

Pronunciation | main stress

2 **a** 🔊 17 Listen and mark the syllables in these words. Then underline the main stress.

a/part/ment
bar/gain

1 countryside	5 mountain
2 complete	6 opinion
3 decide	7 tropical
4 famous	8 village

b Check your answers in a dictionary.

c Now complete the table with words from exercise 2a. Listen again if you want.

Words with two syllables		Words with three syllables	
Stress on 1st syllable	Stress on 2nd syllable	Stress on 1st syllable	Stress on 2nd syllable
bargain			apartment

Grammar | modifiers (*very, quite, really*)

3 Write a sentence with your opinion about these things. Use a modifier and the adjective given.

> not/very   quite   really   very

football/exciting
Football isn't very exciting.

1 theme parks/exciting
_____

2 our teacher/friendly
_____

3 television/relaxing
_____

4 my diet/healthy
_____

5 computer games/interesting
_____

6 skiing/dangerous
_____

7 burgers/unhealthy
_____

8 flea markets/boring
_____

4 Choose an adjective to describe each picture and write a sentence about it with the modifier given.

> big   famous   healthy   tall   interesting   ~~wide~~

1 the river/very

The river is very wide.

2 the police officer's job/very

_____

3 the Empire State building/really

_____

4 the car/not very

_____

5 Brad Pitt/very

_____

6 chicken and potatoes/quite

_____

How to... | talk about where you come from/live

5 **a** 🔘 18 Cover the audioscript. Listen to John talking about his city and answer the questions.

Where is John from?

Edinburgh

1 Where is Edinburgh?

_____

2 What has Edinburgh got?

_____

3 When is there an arts festival in Edinburgh?

_____

4 Which other city is near Edinburgh?

_____

5 What landscapes are there near the city?

_____

6 Does John like Edinburgh? Why?

_____

b Listen again and find phrases that express these ideas. Write them in the table.

How to...	
say where you come from/live	*I come from ... .*
say what kind of place it is and where it's near	
describe the landscape	
give your opinion	

c Listen and check your answers.

AUDIOSCRIPT

Hello, I'm John. I come from Scotland and I live in Edinburgh. That's a large city in the south-east of Scotland. Edinburgh is a really interesting city. It's got a lot of museums, theatres and restaurants, and there's a famous arts festival every summer. I always go to that with my friends. Edinburgh is quite near Glasgow, another huge, interesting city, and there are some lovely lakes and mountains north of the two cities, in the centre of Scotland. I really like Edinburgh because it's a very friendly place and it's a beautiful city, but there are always a lot of tourists in the city and it can be very busy.

Grammar | Past Simple of *to be*

1 Look at the maps and write sentences about Summertown in 1970.

There are offices in Green Street.

There were houses in Green Street.

1 There's a theme park in Lake Road.

_____

2 There's a supermarket in Lake Road.

_____

3 There are apartments in Station Road.

_____

4 There's a museum in Station Road.

_____

5 There's a nightclub in Harley Street.

_____

6 There's a hotel in Harley Street.

_____

7 There's a sports centre in the park.

_____

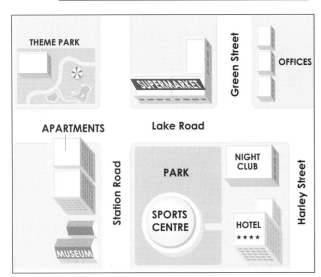

Summertown now

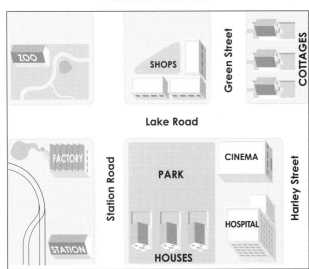

Summertown 1970

2 Write questions about Summertown in 1970. Then answer them.

there/supermarket/Lake Road?

Was there a supermarket in Lake Road?

No, there wasn't. There were shops.

what/there/the park?

What was there in the park?

There were houses in the park.

1 there/factory/Station Road?

_____

_____

2 what/there/Green Street?

_____

_____

3 there/nightclub/Harley Street?

_____

_____

4 there/apartments/Station Road?

_____

_____

5 what/there/next to the cinema?

_____

_____

6 what/there/in the park?

_____

_____

Reading

3 Put the dialogue in the correct order.

☐ I <u>decided</u> to have a sandwich in the office, so I stayed at work at lunchtime.

☐ Oh, I've got a letter from a company in Spain. Can you translate it for me?

1 I really wanted to talk to you yesterday. I phoned you at 8:30 in the morning.

8 Yes, of course I can. Why don't you bring the letter to me this evening?

☐ Oh, it was a lovely day, so I walked to work yesterday. I wasn't at home at 8:30.

☐ No, I visited my friend Rosie in hospital after work. What was the problem anyway?

☐ Yes, it was a nice day. I called you again at lunchtime – I wanted to ask you to come to lunch with me.

☐ Then I tried to call your office at 5:30, but you weren't there.

Grammar | Past Simple of regular verbs: positive

4 **a** Underline all the Past Simple verbs in the dialogue in exercise 3. Do not underline *was*/*were*.

b Now complete the sentences with the underlined verbs in exercise 3.

'Where's Peter?' 'I don't know. I *called* his mobile five minutes ago, but there was no answer.'

1 We _____ for three hours yesterday afternoon – we were really tired in the evening!

2 When we were in Venice last year, we _____ in a really luxurious hotel.

3 We weren't sure what to cook for dinner yesterday, so we _____ to go out and have a pizza.

4 Jack and I _____ our friends in Switzerland last weekend. It was interesting, but very cold there!

5 Allie _____ to study at Oxford University, but her marks weren't very good.

6 We've got tickets for the Lady Gaga concert! I _____ this morning and booked them over the phone.

7 I really _____ to learn all these new words, but I just can't remember them all!

5 Angie is a famous singer. Look at her diary for last week and complete the sentences.

Monday	10	17 plan trip to New York
Tuesday	11	18 play football with boys (afternoon)
Wednesday	12 visit new concert hall 3:00 p.m.	19 TODAY
Thursday	13	20
Friday	14 perform at concert hall 8:30 p.m.	21
Saturday	15 open new supermarket 10:30 a.m.	22
Sunday	16 watch DVD of concert with Mike, 4:00 p.m.	23

Angie *visited the new concert hall* last Wednesday.

1 She _____
_____ last Friday evening.

2 _____
_____ last Saturday morning.

3 _____
_____ on Sunday afternoon.

4 _____
_____ two days ago.

5 _____
_____ yesterday.

6 **a** Complete the text about Luisa's day with the Past Simple form of verbs from the box.

cook   help   play   relax   ~~start~~   walk
watch   work

Luisa's day *started* at 8:00 a.m. yesterday. She
(1) _____ to work at 9:00 and she (2) _____
from 9:30 to 4:30. Then she (3) _____ tennis
with a friend from 4:30 to 5:30. At home she
(4) _____ dinner for her family and then she
(5) _____ her son with his school work. In
the evening, she (6) _____ a DVD and she
(7) _____ .

b Look at the notes. Complete the text about Warren's day.

start – 6:30 a.m.
walk to bus stop – 7:00
wait for bus – 7:15 to 7:30
work – 8:00 to 4:00
repair cars all day
cook dinner for his family
study – 7:30 to 9:30
listen to music

Warren's day

Warren's day *started* at 6:30 a.m. yesterday.
He (1) _____ to the bus stop at (2) _____ .
He (3) _____ fifteen minutes for (4) _____ .
He (5) _____ from 8:00 to (6) _____ .
He (7) _____ . At home he
(8) _____ . He
(9) _____ . In the evening, he
(10) _____ .

Pronunciation | Past Simple endings

7 **a** Look at the text in exercise 6b and find:

three verbs that end in /t/: _____, _____ ,
_____

two verbs that end in /d/: _____ , _____
two verbs that end in /ɪd/: *started* , _____

b 🔘 19 Listen and check your answers.

Listening

AUDIOSCRIPT

A: Hi, Louise. How was your weekend?

B: Great! We went away for the weekend.

A: That's nice. Where to?

B: Barcelona. We flew out on Friday morning and arrived back here late last night. We left Barcelona at about 8:00 yesterday evening, so we had three days there.

A: What's Barcelona like?

B: It's fantastic – really beautiful! We saw some lovely old buildings and visited museums and an art gallery, the Picasso Museum. It's got lots of paintings from when he was young.

A: Was the weekend expensive?

B: Well, yes. We stayed in a good hotel and we ate in quite expensive restaurants. On Saturday evening we met some of Mike's friends for dinner. They took us to a fantastic restaurant up in the hills, but it wasn't cheap! We bought a few things, too – in a huge department store in the centre.

A: Was the weather good?

B: No, it wasn't! It rained a lot of the time, so we spent all day Saturday in museums and lovely indoor markets. But yesterday afternoon was nice, so we walked a lot – we went to a really interesting park. The architect Gaudí designed it. You know, we loved the city and we want to go back.

1 **a** 🔘 20 Cover the audioscript and listen to the conversation. What is it about?

1 a short break at a friend's house ☐

2 a short break in a famous city ☐

3 a visit to an art gallery ☐

b Look at the audioscript and circle four or five words and phrases that helped you choose the answer in exercise 1a.

2 Listen again and decide if the statements are true (T) or false (F). Then correct the false statements.

They had a great weekend. ☐T☐

1 Louise and Mike were away for four days. ☐

_____

2 They went to the Salvador Dalí Museum. ☐

_____

3 They went to a friend's house for dinner on Saturday evening. ☐

_____

4 They spent a lot of money. ☐

_____

5 The weather was good all weekend. ☐

_____

3 Complete the phrases with some of the verbs from the box. You can use some verbs more than once.

arrive   buy   eat   fly   go   have   leave
love   meet   rain   see   spend   stay   take
visit   walk

have a city break

1 _____ from an airport

2 _____ early in the morning

3 _____ in the city at lunchtime

4 _____ in a hotel

5 _____ sightseeing

6 _____ museums

7 _____ round the city

8 _____ friends

9 _____ in a restaurant

10 _____ clothes and shoes

11 _____ money

12 _____ a good time

Grammar | Past Simple: irregular verbs

4 **a** Write the Past Simple form of the verbs from exercise 3 in the table.

Regular	Irregular
arrived	bought

b Make sentences. Use verbs from exercise 4a.

we/Istanbul/2:00 p.m.

We arrived in Instanbul at 2:00 p.m.

1 we/Bristol airport/Friday

_____

2 we/great time

_____

3 we/cheap hotel/city centre

_____

4 Saturday/we/sightseeing

_____

5 we/a lot of museums and galleries

_____

6 we/round the city/afternoon

_____

7 we/lovely fish restaurant/evening

_____

8 we/some clothes and shoes

_____

9 we/a lot of money

_____

10 last month/we/city break/Istanbul

_____

Vocabulary | places in a city, shops

5 Complete the crossword.

Across (grid): 1 H O S P I T A L

Across

1 Doctors and nurses work here.

4 You can drink (and sometimes eat) here.

7 You can buy all your food and drinks here.

8 You can look at paintings here. (2 words)

9 Another place to buy things, often outside.

10 You can buy coats, jackets and scarves here. (2 words)

11 You can take a bus or train from here.

Down

2 You can live here.

3 A nice place for a walk. (see photo)

4 You can put your money here, or take money out.

5 People work here; they produce things.

6 You can look at old things here.

8 We often start our holidays here.

Reading

1 **a** Read the text quickly and answer the question.

How long was Lewis and Clark's journey?

LEWIS AND CLARK

Meriwether Lewis and William Clark are famous American explorers. In 1804 President Thomas Jefferson wanted a map of the western United States because at that time people didn't know the area west of the Mississippi River. Lewis and Clark started from St Louis at the end of 1804 with thirty men and an Indian woman, Sacagawea. The weather was very bad and it was difficult to travel. They stayed for the winter with the Dakota Indians.

After the winter they travelled over the Rocky Mountains. The Indians helped them find the Pacific Ocean at the end of 1805. They discovered many new rivers and mountains and they measured everything for their maps. They started back at the start of 1806 and they finished their journey at the end of the year. They travelled 12,900 kilometres and discovered that North America was a huge place.

b Read the text again and put the events in the correct order. Use a dictionary to check any new words.

They stayed with the Dakota Indians. ☐
They finished their journey to the Pacific Ocean. ☐
The President wanted a map of the western US. ☐ 1
They started back after the winter. ☐
They travelled over the Rocky Mountains. ☐
Lewis and Clark started from St Louis. ☐
The weather was very bad. ☐

c Read the text again and answer the questions.

Why did the President want a map of the western United States?

Because people didn't know the area west of the Mississippi River.

1 How many people were there on the journey?
_____

2 Who helped them find the Pacific Ocean?
_____

3 What did they measure?
_____

4 What did they discover?
_____

Grammar | Past Simple: questions and negatives

2 Look at the answers and complete the questions about the text in exercise 1.

What did the president want in 1804?
He wanted a map of the western United States.

1 _____ from?
They started from St Louis.

2 _____ their journey?
They started their journey in 1804.

3 _____ good?
No, the weather was bad.

4 _____ for the winter?
They stayed with the Dakota Indians.

5 _____ after the winter?
They travelled over the Rocky Mountains.

6 _____ the Pacific Ocean?
They found it at the end of 1805.

7 _____ their journey?
They finished their journey at the end of 1806.

8 _____ about North America?
They discovered that it was a huge place.

3 Complete the questions about the text in exercise 1. Then write short answers.

Did Lewis and Clark start their journey in 1804?
Yes, they did.

1 _____ people know the area west of the Mississippi River?

_____

2 Did the Indians _____ them find the Pacific Ocean?

_____

3 _____ they finish their journey in 1804?

_____

4 Did they _____ 12,900 kilometres?

_____

4 Make negative sentences in the Past Simple.

Christopher Columbus/invent/the computer
Christopher Columbus didn't invent the computer.
Charles Darwin/be/American
Charles Darwin wasn't American.

1 William Shakespeare/write/Don Quixote

_____

2 my great-grandparents/own/a car

_____

3 Queen Elizabeth I/be/married

_____

4 people/have/mobile phones in the 1970s

_____

5 my father/go/to university

_____

6 in the eighteenth century people/wear/jeans

_____

7 I/do/my homework yesterday

_____

Vocabulary | time expressions

5 Complete the sentences with time expressions from the box.

> ago   ~~in 1989~~   in the 1990s   in the 16th century
> last night   last Saturday afternoon   yesterday

Tim Berners-Lee invented the World Wide Web in 1989.

1 There weren't any computers _____ .
2 I lived at home with my parents _____ .
3 It rained all day _____ , but it stopped this morning.
4 I left school two years _____ and I went to work in a supermarket.
5 We watched football on TV _____ and stayed at home all weekend.
6 I didn't sleep well _____ and today I'm tired.

Pronunciation | contrastive stress

6 **a** Underline the stressed words in the answers.

A: Did you see a film?
B: No, we saw a concert.

1 A: Do you like pasta?
   B: No, I like potatoes.
2 A: Are you French?
   B: No, I'm Canadian.
3 A: Is the child hungry?
   B: No, she's thirsty.
4 A: Did you arrive on Friday?
   B: No, we arrived on Thursday.

b 🔘 21 Listen and check your answers.

Reading

7 Read the information about Max Van Der Grinten and complete the questions and answers.

❝I live in Cambridge now, but I wasn't born here and I didn't grow up in England. I was born in Cape Town, in South Africa. I grew up there and I went to school in the centre of the city. At home we spoke Afrikaans, but at my school all the lessons were in English.

When I was young, I wanted to be an engineer. There's a very good engineering course at the University of London, so I decided to come to England when I was eighteen. After university, I got a job in Cambridge, so I decided to stay here. I got married in 2008 and now I'm a British citizen.❞

Did Max *grow up* in England?
No, he *didn't*.

1 _____ he _____ English at home?
   No, he didn't.
2 _____ Max _____ to be an engineer when he was young?
   Yes, he _____ .
3 _____ did he decide to stay in England?
   He _____ to stay in England because he got a _____ in Cambridge.
4 _____ did Max get married?
   He got _____ in 2008.

Grammar
Countable and uncountable nouns

1 Complete the table with words from the box.

> ~~biscuit~~   bread   butter   coin   dishwasher
> lamp   money   receipt   rice   sugar

Countable nouns	Uncountable nouns
biscuit	

much/many/a lot of, a/an, some and any

2 Choose the correct words in *italics*. If both words are correct, circle them both.

I'd like ⓢome/ⓐ lot of cheese, please.

1 How *much/many* meat do you eat every week?
2 There isn't *some/any* milk in the fridge.
3 Simon always takes *a lot of/some* cream in his coffee.
4 Are there *much/many* students in your class?
5 I've got a few minutes, but I haven't got *much/many* time.
6 Have you got *any/a* DVD player?
7 How *much/many* bathrooms are there?
8 Please give me *some/a* carton of orange juice.
9 Can you go to the supermarket, please? Here's *some/any* money.

Object pronouns

3 Complete the sentences with object pronouns.

That's my coffee. It's for *me*.

1 It's John's dictionary. Please give it to _____ .
2 'Is that Marianne and Olaf on the bus?' 'Yes, it's _____ .'
3 That's Eddie's new car. Do you like _____ ?
4 Your girlfriend's on the phone. She wants to speak to _____ .
5 'That's Sophie's sister in the photo.' 'Yes, I know _____ .'
6 That's my credit card. Please give it to _____ .
7 Tony likes our house. He always stays with _____ when he comes to London.
8 'Have some fries with your burger.' 'No, thanks. I don't like _____ .'
9 'Is that Sarah in the shop?' 'Yes, that's _____ .'

there is/there are

4 Complete the dialogue with the correct form of *there is/there are*.

A: I think I'd like to take the apartment, but what furniture *is there* in the living room?
B: Well, (1) _____ a big sofa.
A: (2) _____ a dining table?
B: Yes, (3) _____ . And (4) _____ four dining chairs.
A: Oh, good. (5) _____ a coffee table?
B: No, (6) _____ .
A: OK. (7) _____ any bookshelves?
B: No, (8) _____ .
A: Oh, and what about a TV or a music system?
B: No, (9) _____ any electrical equipment.

Modifiers

5 Choose the correct modifier and write sentences. Use the verb *to be*.

 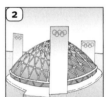

1 (quite/really) my sister   sick   today
My sister is really sick today.

2 (very/not very) the new sports centre   modern
_____

3 (quite/really) this film   boring
_____

4 (quite/really) my diet   unhealthy
_____

5 (very/not very) this beach   popular
_____

have got

6 Make questions with *have got*. Then write short answers.

Alex/an MP3 player? (✗)

A: *Has Alex got an MP3 player?*

B: *No, he hasn't.*

1 you/a microwave? (✗)

A: _____

B: _____

2 Sarah/a credit card? (✓)

A: _____

B: _____

3 your parents/a big garden? (✗)

A: _____

B: _____

4 we/any biscuits? (✓)

A: _____

B: _____

5 the dog/any food? (✓)

A: _____

B: _____

Past Simple

7 **a** Write the Past Simple form of the verbs.

have *had*

1	decide _____	6	produce _____
2	eat _____	7	start _____
3	go _____	8	stay _____
4	leave _____	9	stop _____
5	meet _____	10	want _____
		11	work _____

b Complete the text with the Past Simple form of the verbs in exercise 7a. Use each verb once.

My father was only sixteen when he *left* school. He (1) _____ (not) to study at university because he wanted money, so he (2) _____ in a factory for five years. Then he (3) _____ work and (4) _____ to travel and see some of the world. He (5) _____ to India and he (6) _____ there for ten years. He (7) _____ my mother, they got married and came back to England, where they (8) _____ a business – an Indian restaurant. A lot of people (9) _____ in their restaurant and liked the food. After a few years my parents (10) _____ Indian food in cans for supermarkets and this was very popular. I was very happy when I was a child – with loving parents and lots of money! (11) _____ you _____ a happy time when you were a child?

c Correct the sentences about the text.

The writer's father left school when he was fourteen.
He didn't leave school when he was fourteen. He left school when he was sixteen.

1 He wanted to study at university.

_____

_____

2 He stayed at the factory for ten years.

_____

_____

3 He married a woman in Africa.

_____

_____

4 The writer's parents opened an Indian factory.

_____

_____

5 They produced Indian food for schools.

_____

_____

Vocabulary

8 **a** Write the words from the box in the table.

banana bank bathroom bed cellar
chemist's cola cupboard dining room
fridge kitchen lamb microwave
newsagent's post office potato seafood
station study table

Food and drink	Rooms	Furniture/ equipment	Places in a town
banana			

b Complete the sentences with words from exercise 8a.

We prepare food in the *kitchen*.

1 Excuse me, which _____ does the train to Paris leave from?

2 We don't eat a lot of meat, but we eat fish and _____ nearly every day.

3 We've got a shower in our _____ .

4 We haven't got much time, but we can put a potato in the _____ if you're hungry.

5 My favourite kind of meat is _____ .

6 Can you buy a magazine and a newspaper for me at the _____ ?

7 This room is very untidy. Please put your books in the _____ .

8 Can you get some money from the _____ ?

Reading

1 Read the text quickly. What is it about? Don't worry about the gaps.

1 a new type of banknote ☐

2 a man who tried to steal something ☐

3 a problem with the police ☐

The wrong note

<u>A</u> man was in a Berlin police station last night after he tried to steal (1) _____ 1,000-euro note from (2) _____ car.

The man, a twenty-eight-year-old tourist, noticed (3) _____ note inside the car in a Berlin street. The thief broke into (4) _____ car and took (5) _____ note, but people saw him and called the police. They arrived quickly, caught (6) _____ man and put him in a cell in the police station for the night.

Unfortunately for the man, the note wasn't even a real euro note – euro notes only go up to 500 euros, not 1,000. The note was in fact (7) _____ advertisement for (8) _____ local business. (9) _____ business made the fake 1,000-euro notes to advertise (10) _____ competition – people could win 1,000 euros as the top prize. The thief didn't understand that the note wasn't real!

2 Read the text again and put the events in the correct order.

a The police caught the man. ☐

b A business in Berlin made some fake 1,000-euro notes. ☐ 1

c They took him to the police station. ☐

d He broke into the car and tried to steal the note. ☐

e The man spent the night in a cell in the police station. ☐

f A man noticed one of the 1,000-euro notes in a car. ☐

Lifelong learning | understanding a story

3 **a** Look at the text again and complete the table.

	Words before	Words after	Noun, verb or adjective?
steal	*he tried to*	*1,000 euro note*	*verb*
thief			
broke into			
cell			
fake			

b Match the words in exercise 3a with the meanings.

false, not real
fake

1 went into a house/car to take something
_____

2 a person who takes things and doesn't ask
_____

3 to take something from someone and not ask
_____

4 a room in a police station
_____

4 Answer the questions.

What did the man see?

A 1,000-euro note.

1 Where was the note?

_____

_____

2 Did he know it was a fake note?

_____

_____

3 What did he do?

_____

_____

4 Why did the police come?

_____

_____

5 Where did they take the man?

_____

_____

6 Where did he sleep in the police station?

_____

_____

7 How long did the man stay in the cell?

_____

_____

8 Who made the notes?

_____

_____

9 Why did they make the notes?

_____

_____

10 What was the top prize in the competition?

_____

_____

Vocabulary | phrasal verbs

5 **a** Complete the sentences with the correct form of the phrasal verbs from the box.

> give back   hand in   ~~look at~~   pick up
> pull out   put together   set off

Look at these flowers. Aren't they lovely?

1 We _____ very early on our holiday this morning. We left home at 5:30.

2 The thief _____ all the jewellery when the police caught him.

3 I always _____ the nuts from chocolate and cakes; I don't like nuts.

4 We went to the police and _____ a leather coat yesterday. We found it in the street.

5 The police _____ the clues and worked out who the thief was.

6 We always tell people to _____ their rubbish in the park and put it in the bin.

b There is one phrasal verb in the text in exercise 1. What is it? _____

Grammar | articles

6 Match the articles with their uses.

1 a/an   a when we mention something for the second time

2 the   b when we mention something for the first time

7 Read the story. Choose the correct article in *italics*.

I won (a)/*the* competition last week; the prize was (1) *a/the* digital camera. (2) *A/The* competition was in a newspaper, and it asked people to take photos that showed 'happiness' and send them to (3) *a/the* newspaper by email.

Two or three days later I was in (4) *a/the* park with my two children. I sat on a seat in (5) *a/the* park and at one point I looked up and saw the children. They looked so happy! I remembered (6) *a/the* competition. I had my camera with me, so I took (7) *a/the* photo of the children. When we got home, I decided to send (8) *a/the* photo to (9) *a/the* newspaper. I heard last week that my photo won (10) *a/the* prize! It's very exciting, but why do they give a prize of a digital camera when you need a digital camera to enter the competition?

8 Complete the text in exercise 1 with *a/an* or *the*.

45

Reading

1 **a** Read Katya's blog and choose the correct words in *italics*.

Katya *likes/doesn't like* her classmates. She thinks the lessons are *easy/difficult*.

b Read the text again and answer the questions.

How old is Katya?

Nineteen.

1 Where does Katya study?

_____

2 Where does Katya's teacher come from?

_____

3 How many students are in the class?

_____

4 Which student was a manager before he started the course?

_____

c Complete the sentences.

Alvaro plays in a rock band.

1 _____ has got two children.

2 _____ is really funny and friendly.

3 _____ is quite tanned.

4 _____ is the same age as Katya.

5 _____ isn't very friendly.

6 _____ is bald.

7 _____ is very slim.

2 **a** Use the information from the text in exercise 1 to write labels for the students in the picture.

I started my International Studies course at the university last month. Our teacher, Elizabeth, isn't very friendly. She's middle-aged and she comes from Chicago. My classmates are very nice. There are ten of us in the group – five men and five women. I really like Melanie. She's young and pretty. She's got pale skin and fair hair. Surinda's very friendly. She's short and she's got dark skin. Clara's got short dark hair and she's very slim. Amanda's middle-aged. She's got two children! She's got grey hair and she wears glasses.

The men in my group are all nice. Jeremy's really interesting – he was a manager before he started the course. He's middle-aged and bald, but he's got a little beard. Henry's nineteen, the same age as me. He's got dark skin and a beard, and he wears glasses. I like Dieter a lot – he's very handsome and confident! He's got fair hair and he's quite tanned. Alvaro's also handsome. He's got dark hair, but he hasn't got a beard. He plays in a rock band at the weekends. The last one is Stefan. He isn't very slim, but he's really funny and friendly.

The lessons are quite difficult, but they're very interesting.

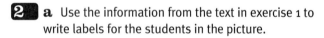

b Complete these sentences about the people with numbers.

Two people have got a beard.

1 _____ people are wearing glasses.

2 _____ people have got fair hair.

3 _____ people are middle-aged.

4 _____ people have got dark hair.

Vocabulary | adjectives (4): people

3 Complete the sentences with adjectives from the box.

> bald   confident   fair   friendly   handsome
> horrible   old   ~~shy~~   unattractive

Sam doesn't like going to parties and meeting new people. He's *shy*.

1   Mrs Barrett is ninety. She's very _____ .

2   Philip doesn't have a handsome face. He's quite _____ .

3   We like our English teacher very much. She's really _____ .

4   Jane is lovely, but I don't like Stephen, her husband. He's _____ .

5   Natalie has blue eyes and long _____ hair.

6   Anna is very _____ . She believes in herself.

7   Harry has beautiful blue eyes and dark hair. He's really _____ .

8   Carl is almost _____ . He has very little hair.

4 Write a sentence describing each of these people.

1   A member of your family.

_____

2   A famous film star or pop star.

_____

3   Your best friend.

_____

4   Your teacher.

_____

Lifelong learning | opposite adjectives

5 Match the adjectives with their opposites.

1   comfortable   a   unfriendly
2   friendly   b   unattractive
3   young   c   horrible
4   shy   d   interesting
5   lovely   e   old
6   pretty   f   fair
7   boring   g   uncomfortable
8   dark   h   confident

Grammar | pronoun *one/ones*

6 Match the words in *italics* in the text (1–5) with the words below.

sports centre   ☐
shopping centre   [1]
swimming pool   ☐
CDs   ☐
salad   ☐

> I love shopping. There is a big shopping centre in our town and there is a small (1) *one* near our house. We go there every Saturday morning. I go to the supermarket and get the food. My husband usually goes to the bookshop and buys CDs. He likes classical (2) *ones*. Then we have lunch. I usually have a small salad and my husband has a large (3) *one*. In the afternoon we go to the sports centre. It's a modern (4) *one* with a gym and a swimming pool – it's a small (5) *one*, but the water is warm. My husband uses the gym and I swim in the pool. I love it!

7 Rewrite the sentences. Use *one* or *ones*.

My girlfriend's got a car, but I haven't got a car.
My girlfriend's got a car, but I haven't got one.

1   I like hot places, but Sally likes cold places.

_____

_____

2   Can I have six large salads and two small salads, please?

_____

_____

3   Do you want the British spelling or the American spelling?

_____

_____

4   We've got three bedrooms. I sleep in the big bedroom.

_____

_____

5   Do you want the blue chairs, the red chairs or the yellow chairs?

_____

_____

6   I'd like four tuna sandwiches and a chicken sandwich, please.

_____

_____

7   Don't wear the red shoes. Wear the black shoes.

_____

_____

Listening

1 a 🔘 22 Cover the audioscript. Listen to the conversation. What are the people talking about?

1 a winter festival ☐
2 a summer festival ☐
3 a fireworks festival ☐

b Listen again and decide if these statements are true (T) or false (F).

Russell went to Moscow. ☐F☐

1 The White Nights is in July. ☐
2 It doesn't snow at that time of year. ☐
3 It isn't dark at night. ☐
4 People sometimes get up early in the morning. ☐
5 There are parties in the daytime. ☐
6 Russell enjoyed his trip. ☐

AUDIOSCRIPT

A: So, Russell, tell me about your trip to Russia. Where did you go exactly?
B: Saint Petersburg.
A: How was it?
B: It was fantastic! We went for the White Nights ...
A: The White Nights? What's that?
B: It's a week or so in June when there's a special festival.
A: Why is it called *White Nights*? Does it snow then?
B: In June? Of course not! No, it's because it's light all the time – all through the night.
A: Really?
B: Yes, it's because the city is really far north.
A: So, it's pretty cold, I suppose.
B: Oh no, it's quite warm, even at night.
A: It sounds really strange.
B: Not really. But you don't know when it's night and when it's day. Sometimes people sleep during the day, then they get up at night and go to parties. And there are amazing concerts and fireworks. We had a lot of fun!

Vocabulary | ordinal numbers and months

2 Answer the questions.

Which date is one month before 5th March?
5th February

1 Which date is two months after 18th September?
_____

2 Which month comes after July?
_____

3 Which date comes after 1st January?
_____

4 Which date is three months before 22nd October?
_____

5 Which date is three weeks after 3rd August?
_____

6 Which month comes before December?
_____

7 Which is the fourth month of the year?
_____

8 How many months end with the letter *y*?
_____

3 Write the dates in *italics* in words.

America's Independence Day is on *4/7*.
the fourth of July

1 Bastille Day, *14/7*, is a holiday in France.
_____

2 William Shakespeare died on *23/4*.
_____

3 St Patrick's Day, *17/3*, is a holiday in Ireland.
_____

4 *26/12* is a holiday in Britain, Canada and Australia.
_____

5 Pedro Alvares Cabral discovered Brazil on *22/4*, 1500.
_____

6 My birthday is on *19/10*.
_____

7 The Second World War started on *1/9* 1939.
_____

8 Martin Luther King's birthday, *15/1*, is a holiday in the US.
_____

Grammar | possessive pronouns

4 Match the things in the picture (A–E) with the statements (1–5).

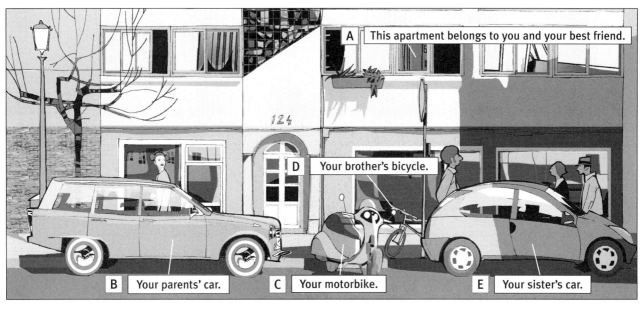

A This apartment belongs to you and your best friend.

D Your brother's bicycle.

B Your parents' car.

C Your motorbike.

E Your sister's car.

1 It's mine. [C]   3 It's hers. ☐   5 It's theirs. ☐
2 It's his. ☐   4 It's ours. ☐

5 Choose the correct words in *italics*.

That's not your book. It's *me/mine*.

1 Can I use *your/yours* car this evening?
2 We can hear *their/theirs* television in our living room.
3 Take one of the pens, they're *our/ours*.
4 Is this dictionary *your/yours*?
5 Don't drink that coffee, it's *her/hers*.
6 We didn't finish *our/ours* dinner.
7 You can use *my/mine* umbrella.
8 Are those *her/hers* trainers?

6 Replace the underlined phrases with expressions from the box.

> are ours   belongs to you   doesn't belong to them
> is mine   is ours   is theirs   ~~isn't mine~~   isn't yours

You can't use that computer. It <u>doesn't belong to me</u>. *isn't mine*

1 I think this book <u>is yours</u>. _____
2 That Nokia phone <u>belongs to me</u>. _____
3 The house on the left <u>belongs to Alice and her husband</u>. _____
4 The big present <u>is for us</u>. _____
5 The DVD player <u>isn't theirs</u>. It's ours. _____
6 That cup of coffee <u>isn't for you</u>, it's for Mauro. _____
7 Those holiday photos <u>belong to us</u>. _____

7 Complete the text with words from the box.

> mine   his   hers   ours   yours   ~~theirs~~

I live in a large apartment with my sister. It belongs to our parents. The furniture doesn't belong to me and my sister – it's all *theirs*, too. But the television and music system are (1) _____ – we bought them together. We've both got mobile phones: (2) _____ is a Nokia. It's got a camera and I can watch videos on it, but (3) _____ isn't very good because it hasn't got a camera. My sister's boyfriend's got a really good phone. He uses (4) _____ in the car because it's got GPS.

Have you got a mobile phone? Can you use (5) _____ to download videos from the Internet?

Pronunciation | /θ/

8 a ● 23 Listen and underline the sound /θ/ in these words.

bir<u>th</u>day

1 third   2 something

b ● 24 Listen. How many times do you hear the sound /θ/ in each sentence?

It's Jane's birthday on Thursday. [2]

1 I'm thirsty – I think I want something to drink. ☐
2 Sean was fourth in the phone-throwing competition. ☐
3 We have three bathrooms on the third floor of our house. ☐
4 Healthy people are usually thin. ☐

8 Seasons

Listening

1 Match the sentences with the people in the picture.

He's eating a burger. [B]

1 They're talking and drinking cola. ☐
2 He's playing football. ☐
3 She's talking on the phone. ☐
4 She's taking photos. ☐
5 They're dancing. ☐
6 They're eating food. ☐
7 She's singing. ☐
8 She's eating crisps. ☐

2 **a** ⬤ 25 Listen to the woman on the phone talking to her friend. Why didn't her friend come to the festival?

b Listen again and match the names with the people in the picture.

Martina [I]

1 Charlie ☐
2 Annette ☐
3 Tanika ☐
4 Clare and Hannah ☐
5 Darren ☐
6 George and Andy ☐
7 Justine ☐
8 Zamboyo ☐

AUDIOSCRIPT

Amy: Martina, it's me, Amy. How are things at the music festival?

Martina: Great! It's really good.

Amy: Oh, I wanted to come, but I'm still feeling awful – really sick.

Martina: That's a shame. We're all here. I'm having a really good time.

Amy: What are you all doing?

Martina: Well, Charlie and Annette are listening to a singer – she's very good. She's singing some pop songs and she's playing the guitar. She's called Tanika. Charlie's eating a burger, but Annette didn't want one. She's eating some crisps.

Amy: Is Clare watching the singer too?

Martina: No, Clare's talking to her friend, Hannah. She met Hannah when we arrived. They're sitting on the grass and drinking cola together. Clare's little brother, Darren, is playing football near them. He isn't listening to the singer!

Amy: Is anything else happening at the moment?

Martina: Yes, there are lots of stalls. George and Andy are walking around the food stalls. They're trying all the different types of food. They aren't talking, just eating! And Justine is watching some dancers.

Amy: Dancers?

Martina: Yes, dancers from Africa, I think. They're called Zamboyo. They're fantastic! They're wearing really colourful costumes. Justine knows one of them. She's taking photos of them.

Amy: And what are you doing?

Martina: Me? I'm talking to you on the phone!

Grammar | Present Continuous

3 **a** Look at the picture again. Who is ...

listening to the singer?   *Charlie and Annette*

drinking cola?   *Clare and Hannah*

1 talking to Amy on the phone?   _____
2 singing some pop songs?   _____
3 talking to Charlie?   _____
4 taking photos?   _____
5 eating a burger?   _____
6 playing football?   _____
7 playing the guitar?   _____
8 sitting on the grass?   _____
9 trying different food?   _____
10 eating crisps?   _____
11 watching the dancers?   _____
12 having a good time?   _____

b Look at the picture. What are the people doing/not doing? Write two sentences for each person/pair.

Martina is talking on the phone.

She's talking to Amy.

1 Charlie _____
_____

2 Annette _____
_____

3 Clare and Hannah _____
_____

4 Darren _____
_____

5 George and Andy _____
_____

6 Justine _____
_____

7 Tanika _____
_____

4 Make questions in the Present Continuous. Then answer them.

Amy/talk to/Justine?

Is Amy talking to Justine?

No, she isn't. She's talking to Martina.

1 Tanika/play/the piano?
_____
_____

2 Charlie and Annette/watch/the dancers?
_____
_____

3 Justine/make/a video?
_____
_____

4 George and Andy/sit down?
_____
_____

5 Zamboyo/sing?
_____
_____

6 Clare/talk/Darren?
_____
_____

7 Darren/play/tennis?
_____
_____

8 Clare and Hannah/eat/crisps?
_____
_____

Pronunciation | sentence stress

5 🔊 26 Listen to the sentences and underline the stressed syllables. Then listen and repeat.

I'm <u>feel</u>ing <u>sick</u>.

1 I'm having a good time.
2 She's playing the guitar.
3 He's eating a burger.
4 He isn't listening.
5 They're sitting on the grass.
6 They aren't talking.
7 We're watching some dancers.

How to... | describe a picture

6 Complete the text about the picture on page 50 with phrases from the box.

> at the back   ~~at the front~~   listening
> of the picture   talking   the left   there are

The picture shows a small village festival. *At the front* of the picture there's a woman (1) _____ on a mobile phone. On (2) _____ is a singer and there are people (3) _____ to her. On the right (4) _____ we can see a group of African dancers. A woman is taking photos of them. There are food stalls (5) _____ of the picture and (6) _____ two men eating the food from the stalls.

Reading

Fashions for this autumn

What's happening in the fashion world this season? We sent Rebecca Langton to Paris to watch the shows and report on the latest trends.

Nothing stays the same for long in the fashion world and this year that's very true. Last year everything was black or grey. No more! This season bright colours are back in fashion – red, orange, yellow and pink are everywhere.

This season's material is wool: wool pullovers, wool skirts and suits. Nowadays wool comes in thousands of bright colours and patterns and designers are using this traditional material in lots of new ways. A thick wool pullover with a loose skirt is a very popular look. With leather boots and bags this is a style you can wear at work or at the weekend. Wool is comfortable to wear and very warm, so this is a great look for cold autumn and winter days.

Designers are also using bright colours and patterns for evening wear. Most designers are using silk and skirts are long and loose, with gold or silver shoes. The style is luxurious and elegant – perfect for parties and special events.

1 **a** Read the text and answer the question.

Which material is popular this season? _____

b Read the text again and answer the questions.

What did the writer see in Paris?

Fashion shows.

1   Which two colours are not fashionable this season?

_____

2   Which material are designers using in new ways?

_____

3   What can you wear with a thick pullover?

_____

4   Why is wool a good material for cold days?

_____

5   What kind of skirts are fashionable for the evenings?

_____

2 **a** Complete the descriptions with words from the box.

~~day~~   evening   gold   leather   loose   shoes   silk   wool

Styles for the _day_:
a thick (1) _____ pullover with a(n)
(2) _____ skirt and (3) _____ boots.
Styles for the (4) _____ :
long, loose (5) _____ skirts with
(6) _____ or silver (7) _____ .

b Look at the text and check your answers.

Vocabulary | clothes

3 **a** Complete the clothes words with *a, e, i, o* or *u*.

c _o_ _a_ t

1 c _ t t _ n	6 l _ g h t	11 s m _ r t
2 f _ r m _ l	7 l _ _ s e	12 s _ _ t
3 j _ c k _ t	8 p _ l l _ v _ r	13 t h _ c k
4 j _ _ n s	9 s h _ r t	14 t _ g h t
5 l _ _ t h _ r	10 s k _ r t	15 w _ _ l

b Write the words from exercise 3a in the table.

Clothes	Adjectives	Materials
coat		

| 1 | _a smart jacket_ | 3 | _____ | 5 | _____ |
| 2 | _____ | 4 | _____ | 6 | _____ |

4 Use an adjective and a clothes word from exercise 3b to write labels for the picture.

5 Write the words from the box in the table. Some words can go in two columns.

> coat   gloves   jeans   pullover   sandals
> scarf   shorts   suit   ~~trainers~~   T-shirt

Summer	Winter	Formal	Informal
			trainers

Grammar | position of adjectives

6 Rewrite the sentences with the word in brackets in the correct place.

Mandy's wearing a pink jacket. (beautiful)
Mandy's wearing a beautiful pink jacket.

1 We bought a comfortable sofa. (leather)
_____

2 In warm weather I prefer casual clothes. (cotton)
_____

3 Do you have a smart suit? (black)
_____

4 Uncle Derek drives an expensive car. (German)
_____

5 Kirsty wore a beautiful wedding dress. (silk)
_____

6 Darren's wearing a wool pullover today. (scruffy)
_____

7 My brother's got a lovely girlfriend. (Japanese)
_____

8 Why are there so many old films on TV these days? (boring)
_____

7 Put the adjectives in these sentences in the correct place.

My best friend lives in an <u>old lovely</u> house. _lovely old_

1 Cara always wears black fashionable clothes.
_____

2 That Swiss watch expensive looks. _____

3 I bought some cotton nice shorts for my summer holiday. _____

4 Those children very polite were to me.
_____

5 How much is that Italian smart jacket in the window? _____

6 Her new boyfriend nice looks. _____

Vocabulary | the weather

1 a Use a group of letters from Box A and a letter or group of letters from Box B to make weather words.

Box A ~~cloud~~ co fog rain sno su wa win

Box B dy gy ing ld nny rm wing ~~y~~

cloud + y = cloudy

1 _____ 4 _____

2 _____ 5 _____

3 _____ 6 _____

7 _____

b Complete the sentences with weather words from exercise 1a.

1 It's *windy* and _____ in the centre.

2 It's _____ and _____ in the north.

3 It's _____ and _____ in the south.

4 It's _____ in the west.

5 It's _____ in the east.

Pronunciation | /ɒ/ and /əʊ/

2 a 🔘 27 Listen to each sentence twice. Are the underlined sounds /ɒ/ or /əʊ/? Write *1* for /ɒ/ and *2* for /əʊ/ above each sound.

    2

1 Joan wears new cotton tops under her old coat.

2 I lost my watch in the post office.

3 I need some new clothes to go to college in October.

4 It's very hot in Australia, but it's snowing and cold in Poland.

b Listen again and check your answers.

Reading

3 a Read the text and tick (✓) the correct columns.

	Good for us	Bad for us	Good and bad
the sun			
hot weather			
cold weather			

Weather wise

Can the weather really affect our health and our moods? Read on and find out!

The sun

- The sun can be good for us. It gives us vitamin D. This is very important for young people when they are growing.

- But the sun can also be bad for us. A lot of sun can hurt our skin very badly – a good suntan really is not healthy.

Hot weather

- Hot weather can be bad for us. We lose water from our bodies and that can be dangerous. It's a good idea to drink a lot of water when it's hot.

- Very hot weather can also affect our moods. In hot weather people often get tired, have headaches and sleep badly. It can also affect people with depression quite badly.

Cold weather

- A lot of old people have problems when it's very cold because their body temperature falls quickly and they become sick.

- Some people become very depressed in cold, dark weather. They can't sleep and they don't eat a lot.

- Cold weather can be good for us, too: people often feel very strong and healthy in the mountains because the cold air is very clean and relaxing.

b Read the text again and decide if these statements are true (T) or false (F).

It is healthy to have a nice suntan. [F]

1 Hot weather is often good for people with depression. ☐

2 The cold can affect old people very badly. ☐

3 Depressed people sometimes don't sleep very well. ☐

4 Many people think cold mountain air is very depressing. ☐

Lifelong learning | nouns and adjectives

4 Complete the table with nouns or adjectives from the text in exercise 3a.

Nouns	Adjectives
health	healthy
importance	(1) _____
(2) _____	suntanned
(3) _____	depressed
sickness	(4) _____
darkness	(5) _____

Grammar | Present Simple and Present Continuous

5 **a** Read the dialogue and answer the questions.

Meera: Hello, Carmen. (1) <u>What are you doing</u> here?

Carmen: Hi! (2) <u>I'm waiting</u> to go on the sunbed. (3) <u>I'm trying</u> to get a good suntan before we go on holiday.

Meera: Really? It isn't healthy to have a suntan, you know.

Carmen: Yes, I know you need to be careful. (4) <u>I always spend</u> just ten minutes on the sunbed. (5) <u>I never stay</u> for very long. You aren't here for the sunbed, then, Meera?

Meera: Oh, no. (6) <u>I'm meeting</u> my fitness instructor. There he is.

Carmen: Oh, (7) <u>do you often come</u> to the gym?

Meera: Yes, (8) <u>I use the gym</u> three or four times a week.

Carmen: Wow! You're very fit!

Where are Meera and Carmen?
At the gym.

1 What is Carmen doing now?

_____

2 How much time does she usually spend on the sunbed?

_____

3 What is Meera doing now?

_____

4 How often does she use the gym?

_____

b Look at the <u>underlined</u> phrases in the dialogue and write the numbers on the correct line.

Actions happening now: *1,* _____

Actions that happen regularly: *4,* _____

6 Look at the pictures and complete the sentences about Jason. Use phrases from the box.

Jason lives in the city and he works in a department store. Every day …

> eat a burger with friends   play computer games
> sell men's clothes   ~~take the bus to work~~

1 *he takes the bus to work.*
2 _____
3 _____
4 _____

This week Jason is on holiday. What's he doing?

> eat fish at a restaurant
> play football on the beach
> ~~sunbathe on the beach~~   swim in the sea

5 *He's sunbathing on the beach.*
6 _____
7 _____
8 _____

The future of the book

Do you like books? Do you like touching the paper? Well, enjoy it now because the e-book is coming!

As long ago as the early 1990s books were available in digital form. It was possible to go online and read one, but obviously, that isn't very convenient. Then, in the late 1990s, the first e-book readers arrived. Now there are several e-book readers such as Amazon's Kindle and the iPad, so you can read your e-books in digital form anywhere.

What's so good about e-books? Well, they're better than real books in several ways. They're more convenient: you can put thousands of books on an e-book reader. They're smaller and lighter to carry than several real books – much better

when you go on holiday! Digital books are usually cheaper than physical books and they're more versatile – you can change the size of the text on the screen, for example, or you can change the language.

Why don't we all have e-books? There are a few problems: the e-book reader is still quite expensive – more expensive than buying a lot of books – and it's heavier than a real book if you want to take it to work, for example. Real books are more hard-wearing than e-book readers. If a real book falls onto the ground, it doesn't break, but an e-book reader can break. Real books are more attractive, too – you can wrap them and give them as presents.

So, e-book or real book? For now, at least, we can choose ...

Reading

1 **a** Look quickly at the photos and text. Don't read the text yet. What two things does the text compare? _____

b Read the text and tick (✓) the correct boxes.

	e-book reader	a real book
more convenient	✓	☐
1 heavier	☐	☐
2 cheaper	☐	☐
3 more versatile	☐	☐
4 hard-wearing	☐	☐
5 more attractive	☐	☐

2 Read the text again and answer the questions.

When was the first e-book available?

In the early 1990s.

1 What is Kindle?

_____

2 When did Kindle arrive?

_____

3 How many books can you put on an e-book reader?

_____

4 What can you do with the language?

_____

5 What can happen if an e-book reader falls on the ground?

_____

Vocabulary | news sources

3 The verbs in these sentences are wrong. Underline the mistakes. Then correct them.

I often <u>watch</u> blogs to find the news. *read*

1 Do you use online much for the news? _____

2 Older people like to read the radio. _____

3 I use news programmes on TV because they're more exciting. _____

4 On Sunday mornings we have a nice breakfast and watch the newspapers. _____

5 All my friends listen to Twitter a lot. _____

Grammar | comparison of adjectives

4 Make sentences. Use the comparative form of the adjectives.

e-books/versatile/real books

E-books are more versatile than real books.

1 real books/attractive/e-books

_____

2 e-book readers/light/several real books

_____

3 coats/warm/jackets

_____

4 Chicago/windy/New York

_____

5 Japanese/difficult/English

_____

6 Santiago/small/Mexico City

_____

5 **a** Use an adjective from Box A and an adjective from Box B to make pairs of opposite adjectives.

Box A
> cold   difficult   ~~formal~~   loose   quiet
> smart   ugly   unhealthy   untidy

Box B
> casual   easy   handsome   healthy
> hot   ~~informal~~   noisy   tidy   tight

formal – informal

1 _____
2 _____
3 _____
4 _____
5 _____
6 _____
7 _____
8 _____

b Use pairs of adjectives from exercise 5a to compare the people and things in the pictures.

A $2 + 2 = 4$

B $3x = \dfrac{5y}{x}$

1 *Sum A is easier than sum B. Sum B is more difficult than sum A.*

Ken   Mike

2 _____

living room   bedroom

3 _____
_____

Emma   Caroline

4 _____
_____

Harriet   Harry

5 _____
_____

Egypt   Greenland

6 _____
_____

6 Write the comparative form of the adjectives.

popular   *more popular than*

1 young   _____
2 nice   _____
3 exciting _____
4 cold   _____
5 pretty   _____

Pronunciation | /ə/ in comparatives

7 **a** 🔊 28 Listen and underline the /ə/ sounds in the comparatives in exercise 6.

b Listen again and repeat.

How to... | give your opinion

8 Complete the dialogue. Use one word in each gap.

A: Look! I've got an iPad!

B: Oh, wow! When did you get that?

A: At the weekend.

B: What do you think *of* it?

A: Well, it's good and easy to use, but I don't (1) _____ it very exciting like some people do.

B: Yes, I (2) _____ that some people want every new thing that comes out. Isn't it just another laptop?

A: No, it's more than that. (3) _____ my opinion, it's better than a laptop. You can use it for e-books, for example.

B: That's good, but I (4) _____ think I'd like an iPad. I've got my Kindle. Do you (5) _____ it's better than Kindle?

A: It's more versatile, sure.

Vocabulary | films

1 **a** Find eight more types of film in the word square (→↓↘).

S	Y	D	X	X	F	Y	A	O	A	S	M	Y	C
R	N	O	H	N	F	U	T	T	D	N	U	R	A
Q	P	C	T	O	O	F	J	Z	V	N	S	Y	R
B	T	U	O	H	R	D	V	I	E	Q	I	H	T
G	H	M	Y	M	R	R	U	U	N	W	C	S	O
U	R	E	Q	A	E	B	O	T	T	S	A	R	O
B	I	N	O	F	D	D	V	R	U	G	L	M	N
F	L	T	O	L	T	Z	Y	O	R	P	A	A	S
I	L	A	I	S	S	E	C	Q	E	R	Y	E	G
L	E	R	L	O	V	E	S	T	O	R	Y	G	Y
N	R	Y	J	T	T	O	A	J	R	X	C	B	W
S	C	I	E	N	C	E	F	I	C	T	I	O	N

b Match the types of film from exercise 1a with the descriptions.

Girls and boys meet and fall in love. a *love story*

1 It's a funny film. a _____
2 It's scary. Horrible things happen.
   a _____ film
3 The people aren't real. They're pictures.
   a _____
4 The story is exciting. There's lots of action.
   an _____ film
5 There's singing and dancing in this.
   a _____
6 Sometimes people leave Earth in this type of film.
   a _____ film
7 You don't know the answer before the end.
   a _____
8 This film contains real facts and information.
   a _____

Grammar | superlative adjectives

2 Find and underline the mistakes. Then correct them.

Mr Sanders is <u>the most rich</u> man in our town.
the richest

1 Salima is the most best student in the class.
   _____
2 The Pacific is the bigger ocean in the world.
   _____
3 My sister's baby is newest member of our family.
   _____
4 I bought the most cheap camera in the shop.
   _____
5 Alicia is the most attractivest girl in the group.
   _____

3 Write sentences. Use adjectives from the box.

clever	heavy	~~rich~~	romantic	tall	young

Martin has $30,000, Justin has $70,000 and Frank has $55,000.
Justin is the richest man.

1 Jane is 1.90 m, Susan is 1.73 m and Maria is 1.82 m.
   _____
2 Sarah's child is three months old, Annabel's child is four months old and Yvonne's child is two months old.
   _____
3 Dave, Karin and Luis are all at university. Dave got 86 percent in his exams, Karin got 74 percent and Luis got 92 percent.
   _____
4 Chris's weight is 72 kilos, Jan's weight is 67 kilos and Antonio's weight is 83 kilos.
   _____
5 Paul buys his girlfriend flowers on her birthday, William buys his girlfriend flowers every month and Peter buys his girlfriend flowers once a week.
   _____

4 **a** Make sentences.

rich/actor/Tom Cruise
The richest actor is Tom Cruise.

1 old/tree/in Sweden
   _____
   _____
2 loud/rock band/Green Day
   _____
   _____
3 big/passenger plane/the Airbus A380
   _____
   _____
4 dry/desert/the Atacama Desert in Chile
   _____
   _____
5 fast/animal/the cheetah
   _____
   _____
6 dangerous/roads/in India
   _____
   _____
7 high/mountain/Mount Everest
   _____
   _____
8 poisonous/animal/a frog
   _____
   _____

b Make superlative sentences giving your opinion.

interesting/film

I think the most interesting film is Avatar.

1 bad/film

_____

2 good/actor

_____

3 funny/cartoon

_____

4 untidy/person in my family

_____

5 boring/TV programme

_____

6 beautiful/place in my country

_____

Reading

5 Read the text opposite quickly and write *1*, *2* or *3*.

Which film/films …

1 are about a family?   ☑ 2 ☐

2 has some horror in it? ☐

3 is about a writer? ☐

4 are from the US? ☐ ☐

5 is Dan's favourite? ☐

6 Match the definitions with the underlined words in the text.

go away and not come back *disappear*

1 a film about ordinary people _____

2 something that hurts people, e.g. when two cars hit each other _____

3 someone who works at a high level for a company _____

4 very sure _____

7 Read the text again and answer the questions. Write full sentences.

Which film does Dan think is the best film of the three?

Dan thinks The Ghost *is the best film.*

1 Which does he think is the funniest film?

_____

2 Which does he think is the most interesting?

_____

3 Which does he think is the most unusual?

_____

4 Which is the longest film of the three?

_____

5 Which is the shortest film?

_____

8 Read the text again and complete the table.

Film	Type	Time	Dan's rating (✱)
1	thriller		
2			
3			

Dan's film choice

This week I look at three films that are not really the same at all, but have some comedy in them.

1 The Ghost *(thriller, US, 127 minutes)*

Starring Pierce Brosnan (ex-James Bond) and Ewan McGregor

The Ghost (Ewan McGregor) is a writer. He gets the job of writing an ex-British Prime Minister's life story, after the first writer dies in an accident. But was it really an accident?

My opinion: a really interesting thriller, with some comedy

2 It's a wonderful (after)life

(comedy horror, UK, 100 minutes)

Starring Sanjeev Baskar and Goldy Notay

Mrs Sethi wants to find a husband for her daughter, who is not very pretty and has strong opinions. She introduces her daughter to several men, but they all disappear after eating at Mrs Sethi's house.

My opinion: very funny, but not very interesting; a silly idea

3 The Joneses *(comedy drama, US, 96 minutes)*

Starring David Duchovny (from *The X-Files*) and Demi Moore

Steve and Kate Jones have the perfect family and the perfect life. Kate is beautiful and fashionable. Steve is a rich, successful businessman. Their children are the cleverest in the school. Everyone wants to be like them, but are they so perfect?

My opinion: a really unusual idea, a bit like *The Truman Show* in some ways, not very funny

Listening

1 a 🔘 29 Cover the audioscript. Listen and match 1–5 with the places (a–e).

1	photographs of the fall of the Berlin Wall	a	Philharmonie
		b	Columbiahalle
2	Georg Grosz	c	Alexanderplatz
3	The Cranberries	d	Sage-Club
4	house music	e	Academy of Arts
5	classical music		

b Listen again and answer the questions.

How much does it cost to visit the exhibition of photographs of the Berlin Wall?

It's free.

1 What nationality was the artist Georg Grosz?

_____

2 Which day is the Georg Grosz exhibition closed?

_____

3 Where can you buy tickets to see the Cranberries?

_____

4 Where can you dance?

_____

5 The Berlin Philharmonic is performing works by two famous composers. What are their names?

_____

c Look at the audioscript and check your answers.

AUDIOSCRIPT

Welcome to the Berlin English language tourist information line. This week there are a number of events and exhibitions taking place in the city.

At Alexanderplatz there is a free open-air exhibition of photographs of the fall of the Berlin Wall in 1989. It's open twenty-four hours a day and there are explanations in German and English. At the Academy of Arts there is a special exhibition of the work of famous German artist Georg Grosz. Entrance is five euros and it's open Tuesday to Sunday from eleven to eight in the evening.

For rock music lovers, the Cranberries are appearing at Columbiahalle on Saturday. You can buy tickets from the website. If you want to dance, the very fashionable Sage-Club has some of the best house music in the city. It's at 76 Köpenicker Straße.

For classical music lovers, the world-famous Berlin Philharmonic orchestra is performing at the Philharmonie. The programme this week includes works by Beethoven and Mozart. You can buy tickets for the concerts at the box office between ...

Grammar | *like/love/hate/prefer*

2 Choose the correct words to complete the sentences.

I prefer _____ to tea.
a drink coffee **(b coffee)** c of coffee

1 I like novels, but my brother prefers _____ newspapers.
   a read b reading c reads

2 Karol hates _____ his car.
   a washes b the wash c washing

3 Does he _____ playing tennis?
   a prefer swimming b prefer swim to
   c prefer swimming to

4 Do you like _____ football on TV?
   a watch b watching c watched

5 Samuel prefers cars _____ motorbikes.
   a of b than c to

6 I really _____ rap music – it's terrible!
   a hating b hate c hate it

7 I usually prefer _____ .
   a read than write
   b reading to writing
   c read to write

8 We don't like _____ very much.
   a dance b dancing c to dancing

3 Complete the sentences with words from the box.

> don't like ~~like~~ listen listening love
> prefer stay staying swimming than to

I *like* visiting foreign countries.

1 I _____ Banksy's art – it's fantastic!

2 What do you want to drink? Do you _____ tea or coffee?

3 Kim loves _____ to rock music when she's driving her car.

4 I _____ coffee – it gives me a headache!

5 My sister loves her mobile phone more _____ her family!

6 I love _____ in bed late on Sunday mornings.

7 I prefer not to _____ to the radio in the car.

8 We prefer beach holidays _____ city holidays.

9 Do you like _____ in the sea?

10 I prefer to _____ at home at the weekend.

How to... | talk about preferences

4 **a** Tick (✓) the sentence that has the same meaning as the first sentence.

I prefer Julie to Jane.

a I like Jane more than Julie. ☐

b I like Julie more than Jane. ☑

1 I hate Banksy's art.

   a I don't like Banksy's art. ☐

   b I love Banksy's art. ☐

2 Do you like beef more than chicken?

   a Do you prefer beef to chicken? ☐

   b Do you prefer chicken to beef? ☐

3 Do you like jazz more than classical music?

   a Do you hate jazz or classical music? ☐

   b Do you prefer jazz to classical music? ☐

b Find and underline the mistakes. Then correct them.

I prefer comedy films ~~from~~ action films. *to*

1 Jimmy love coffee in the morning. _____

2 Do you liking classical music? _____

3 Do you prefer eat Turkish food or Italian food? _____

4 Caroline likes meat more of vegetables. _____

5 We hating rap music. _____

6 Sarah prefers tea of coffee. _____

7 My brother hates the walking. _____

8 Do you prefer reading to watch TV? _____

5 Rewrite the sentences using *prefer*.

I like Monet more than Picasso.

I prefer Monet to Picasso.

She thinks drinking water is better than drinking fruit juice.

She prefers drinking water to drinking fruit juice.

1 Dario likes traditional art more than modern art.

_____

_____

2 The children are more interested in playing than in reading.

_____

_____

3 I think adventure films are more exciting than horror films.

_____

_____

4 Clara watches television more than she listens to music.

_____

_____

5 We hardly ever visit museums, but we often go to concerts.

_____

_____

6 I like Italian food, but my favourite food is French.

_____

_____

Pronunciation | *yes/no* questions

6 🔊 30 Listen to these questions and answers. Does the voice go up (↗) or down (↘) at the end? Listen to the example first.

A: Do you like it? ↗

B: No, I don't. ↘

1 A: Is she his new girlfriend?

   B: No, she isn't.

2 A: I bought a new phone.

   B: Was it expensive?

3 A: Are you married?

   B: Yes, I am.

4 A: I don't like poems.

   B: Do you like novels?

5 A: Is he handsome?

   B: Yes, he is.

Grammar
Articles

1 Complete the text with *a* or *the*.

Dear Lilian

We're having a fantastic holiday here in Krakow! We're staying in <u>a</u> great hotel near the centre of (1) _____ city. (2) _____ hotel has got a swimming pool on the top floor. We had a swim in (3) _____ pool this morning, but the water was a bit cold!

There are lots of things to see in (4) _____ city. There's (5) _____ castle and there are lots of interesting museums. We went to (6) _____ castle yesterday and spent four hours there – it's huge! We even had lunch in (7) _____ castle – it's got a great café. There's (8) _____ huge square in the centre of Krakow, full of restaurants and bars. There's (9) _____ lovely old church there as well. We had dinner in (10) _____ square last night – pizza and ice cream; not very Polish, I'm afraid!

Kieran

Pronoun *one*/*ones* and possessive pronouns

2 Find a noun or phrase in each sentence where it is better to use a pronoun. <u>Underline</u> the noun/phrase. Then write the correct pronoun.

I love apples, especially red <u>apples</u>. *ones*
This is your coffee and this is <u>my coffee</u>. *mine*

1 The party isn't at my parents' house – it's at our house. _____
2 This isn't your wallet – it's my wallet. _____
3 Those flowers are lovely, especially the pink flowers. _____
4 'Which is the bus for the centre?' 'The bus on the right.' _____
5 'Is this their house?' 'No, the one with the blue door is their house.' _____
6 'Is this your bag?' 'No, it's your bag!' _____

Present Continuous

3 Make sentences in the Present Continuous.
what/Jean/wear/today?
What is Jean wearing today?
Andy/not study/this evening
Andy isn't studying this evening.

1 Dan and Gemma/make/a Chinese meal
_____
2 what/Steve/do/in the garden?
_____
3 Laura/wear/a long skirt/this evening
_____
4 what/you/watch/on TV?
_____
5 Mum/not speak/to Dad/at the moment
_____
6 the boys/play/tennis/in the park
_____
7 Our daughter/sleep/in her room
_____
8 where/you/plan/to go on holiday?
_____
9 I/not have/a very good time
_____
10 what/you/carry/in that bag?
_____

Present Simple and Present Continuous

4 Choose the correct words in *italics*.

| From: | Karen |
| To: | Emily |

Hi Emily

How are you? I *send*/*'m sending* this email to ask if you are busy this afternoon. If not, can you come to my house for coffee?

As you know, Gerry and I (1) *usually work*/*are usually working* during the day and we (2) *don't get*/*aren't getting* home before six in the evening, but today I (3) *'ve*/*'m having* a day at home. I (4) *wait*/*'m waiting* for a new cooker! We bought it on Saturday and it (5) *comes*/*'s coming* today, I hope. The shop (6) *brings*/*is bringing* it sometime today, but I don't know when exactly. Our old cooker broke last week and we need a new one because we both (7) *like*/*are liking* cooking. Gerry and I (8) *cook*/*are cooking* every evening, so it's very difficult without a cooker. So, (9) *do you do*/*are you doing* anything today?

Love
Karen

Position of adjectives

5 Add an adjective to each description in the correct place.

> American   comfortable   friendly   German
> old   scruffy   ~~silk~~   tight

1   a beautiful dress   *a beautiful silk dress*
2   an Italian painting   _____
3   a wool pullover   _____
4   an expensive car   _____
5   a Chinese student   _____
6   a leather sofa   _____
7   a famous statue   _____
8   a white T-shirt   _____

Comparison of adjectives and superlative adjectives

6 Look at the table and make sentences. Use the comparative and superlative form of the adjectives.

	Age	Height	Weight
Joe	33	1.80 m	82 kg
Ian	26	1.85 m	75 kg
Mac	40	1.95 m	80 kg

Joe/Ian: short
Joe is shorter than Ian.
Joe/Ian/Mac: old
Mac is the oldest.

1   Ian/Mac: heavy
    _____
2   Joe/Mac: old
    _____
3   Joe/Ian/Mac: tall
    _____
4   Joe/Mac: short
    _____
5   Joe/Ian/Mac: young
    _____
6   Joe/Ian: heavy
    _____
7   Joe/Ian/Mac: short
    _____
8   Ian/Mac: young
    _____
9   Joe/Ian: old
    _____
10 Joe/Ian/Mac: heavy
    _____

like/love/hate/prefer

7 Find and underline the mistakes. Then correct them.

Denis prefers cycle to playing tennis. *cycling*

1   We prefer old films than modern films. _____
2   Caroline likes go to rock concerts in her free time.
    _____
3   We hate to eating meat – we always eat fish.
    _____
4   Matt loves play football on Saturday afternoons.
    _____
5   I hate to doing grammar exercises! _____
6   Do you prefer swim or sunbathing? _____

Vocabulary

8   a Underline the odd one out.

foggy   windy   pretty

1   thriller   ballet   cartoon
2   tight   trainers   trousers
3   novel   pullover   poetry
4   first   sixteenth   slim
5   comedy   modern   traditional
6   suit   hat   hot
7   sandals   formal   smart

b Complete the sentences with the underlined words from exercise 8a.

Cathy is small, fair and very *pretty*.

1   It's always _____ in the Mediterranean in the summer.
2   Alison is very _____ now – she lost a lot of weight last year.
3   I don't like any kind of dancing, so I don't like _____ .
4   Put your _____ on – it's very cold today.
5   Everyone likes _____ films when they feel sad because they laugh and feel better.
6   This skirt is too _____ – can I try a bigger size, please?
7   I usually wear _____ when I go to the beach.

Reading

Technology review

Citybug electric scooter

Star rating ★★★★★

Commuting in big cities is getting more and more difficult. You can't park cars. Buses are slow. Trains are expensive and crowded. What can you do?

Cycling is the answer for many people. It's great if your city streets are flat and you are fit and have lots of *energy*. But many people get tired and it's very difficult to cycle up *hills*.

So, if you want to find an easy way to commute and you don't have a lot of energy, try the Citybug electric *scooter*.

The Citybug has an electric engine with a *top speed* of fourteen miles per hour (twenty-two kilometres per hour). It loves going up hills! Because the Citybug is electric, you don't need to go to the *petrol station*! You just *connect* the Citybug to the electricity in your house for one or two hours. So it's very cheap. Riding the Citybug is easy, but the seat and the *wheels* are small, so it isn't very comfortable. Of course it isn't fast and it weighs 21 kg, so it's quite heavy. But it's easy to park and you don't need a driving licence, so adults or children can use it.

Click here to go to our price comparison page for the latest prices.

---

1 **a** Look at the text. Where is it from?

1. a newspaper ☐
2. a magazine ☐
3. an Internet page ☐

b Read the text. Match the descriptions with the words in *italics* in the text.

small mountains _hills_

1. a place where you can buy petrol for your car _____
2. the fastest speed _____
3. round things that turn when they move _____
4. the power to make your body move _____
5. small motorbike _____
6. join two things together _____

c Read the text again and write notes in the table. Use words from the box in your answers.

> cheap   ~~comfortable~~   driving licence   easy
> ~~energy~~   fast   heavy   park   petrol station

Citybug electric scooter	
Advantages	**Disadvantages**
You don't need a lot of energy.	*It isn't very comfortable.*

Vocabulary | transport

2 **a** Match the forms of transport with the photos.

1 an electric tram ☐ D 4 a bicycle ☐
2 a taxi ☐ 5 a motorbike ☐
3 a water bus ☐ 6 a helicopter ☐

b Read the descriptions and write a form of transport from exercise 2a.

It has a big engine, but only two wheels. *a motorbike*

1 It flies in the air and it has an engine.

_____

2 It has two wheels, but it doesn't have an engine.

_____

3 We use it in the city, but it travels on water, not on roads. _____

4 It's a car and you pay money to the driver at the end of the journey. _____

5 It's like a bus, but it runs on metal tracks in the street like a train. _____

3 Underline the odd one out.

platform   station   <u>car</u>   train

1	flight	airport	long-haul	garage
2	traffic	boat	commuting	rush hour
3	ticket	passenger	first class	suburb
4	water	bicycle	water bus	boat

Grammar | *-ing* form as noun

4 Make sentences using the *-ing* form. Use an adjective from the box in each sentence.

> dangerous difficult ~~easy~~ healthy
> relaxing scary

send/text messages
Sending text messages is easy.

1 watch/horror films

_____

2 eat/lots of fruit and vegetables

_____

3 drive/in fog

_____

4 learn/a foreign language

_____

5 swim/in warm water

_____

5 Rewrite the sentences using the *-ing* form.

It's cheap to travel by underground in Paris.
Travelling by underground in Paris is cheap.

1 It's difficult to park a car in big cities.

_____

2 It's easy to get information from the Internet.

_____

3 It's romantic to send flowers to your wife.

_____

4 It's nice to get an email from your best friend.

_____

5 It's interesting to watch the news on TV.

_____

How to... | book a train ticket

6 Choose the correct words in *italics*.

Stephen: Do you sell train (tickets)/*flights* for Holland and Belgium? We'd like two tickets from Amsterdam (1) *at/to* Brussels, please.

Travel agent: OK. What is your departure date?

Stephen: Saturday, 21st of this month.

Travel agent: (2) *There/One-way* or return?

Stephen: Return. We'd like to come back on Saturday, 28th.

Travel agent: (3) *Standard/Other* class or first class?

Stephen: How much (4) *costs/is* first class?

Travel agent: €150.

Stephen: Is it a (5) *long-haul/direct* train?

Travel agent: No, it (6) *stops/arrives* in The Hague.

Stephen: What time does it leave?

Travel agent: It leaves Amsterdam (7) *in/at* 10:30.

Listening

1 **a** 🔊 31 Listen to an extract from a job interview. What is the job?

b Listen again. Tick (✓) the places Della has been to and cross (✗) the places she hasn't been to.

1	New York	✓	
2	Washington	☐	
3	Rio de Janeiro	☐	
4	Bangkok	☐	
5	Singapore	☐	
6	Sydney	☐	
7	San Antonio	☐	
8	Rimini	☐	

c Listen again and write when she went to three of the places in exercise 1b.

Rio de Janeiro: _____

_____

_____

Grammar | Present Perfect with *been*: *I/you/we/they*

2 Answer the questions for Della. Then write true answers about you.

1 Have you been on a package holiday?

Della: *Yes, I have.*

You: _____

2 Have you been on an adventure holiday?

Della: _____

You: _____

3 Have you been to any holiday resorts?

Della: _____

You: _____

3 **a** Complete the dialogue with words from the box. You can use some words more than once.

> been   have   haven't   've   went

Int 1: So, Della, tell us about your travel experiences.

Della: Well, I've been to lots of different places around the world.

Int 1: Where exactly have you *been*?

Della: I've been to New York and Washington. And I (1) _____ to Rio de Janeiro last winter.

Int 1: What about Asia? (2) _____ you been to Bangkok?

Della: No, I (3) _____ never been there. But I've been to Singapore.

Int 1: What about Sydney?

Della: Er, no. I (4) _____ been there.

Int 2: That's all very interesting, but have you (5) _____ to any holiday resorts?

Della: Yes, I (6) _____ been to San Antonio in Ibiza. And I've been to Rimini in Italy.

Int 2: When did you go there?

Della: Well, I went to Rimini when I was at university. And I (7) _____ to San Antonio last summer.

Int 2: Was that a package holiday?

Della: Yes, it was.

Int 1: Have you (8) _____ on any adventure holidays?

Della: No, I (9) _____ .

Int 2: So, why do you want to be a holiday rep?

Della: Well, there was a holiday rep at the resort in San Antonio. She was really good. That's the reason I applied for this job!

b Listen again and check your answers.

4 Match 1–7 with a–g to make sentences.

1 Have you been   a go there last year?
2 Yes, they went there   b there twice.
3 Yes, I've been   c I haven't.
4 No,   d to Greece?
5 Yes,   e been there.
6 Did you   f in 2010.
7 No, I haven't   g I have.

5 Make positive sentences (✓), negative sentences (✗) and questions (?) in the Present Perfect.

I/horse-riding (✗)
I haven't been horse-riding.

you/on a long-haul flight (?)
Have you been on a long-haul flight?

1 I/bungee jumping (✓)
   _____

2 we/to Bangkok (✗)
   _____

3 you/to London (?)
   _____

4 they/on a package holiday (?)
   _____

5 John and Julie/to Australia (✗)
   _____

6 I/on an adventure holiday (✗)
   _____

7 our parents/to Florida (✓)
   _____

8 you/to an IMAX cinema (?)
   _____

9 we/hiking in the mountains (✓)
   _____

10 your cousins/to Disneyland (?)
   _____

6 Write questions in the Present Perfect. Then write true answers about you.

Have you been to a circus?
No, I haven't./Yes, I have.
I went last year.

Pronunciation | /ɪ/

7 a 🔵 32 First listen to the underlined sounds in the examples. Then listen to the underlined sound in each sentence and tick (✓) the correct box.

/ə/   /ɪ/
H<u>a</u>ve you b<u>ee</u>n to England?

       /ɪ/ /ə/
Yes, I've b<u>ee</u>n t<u>o</u> London.

		/ɪ/	/ə/
1	I haven't been to R<u>i</u>mini.	☐	☐
2	Have you b<u>ee</u>n to Australia?	☐	☐
3	We've b<u>ee</u>n bungee jumping.	☐	☐
4	Have you been on <u>a</u> horse?	☐	☐
5	Have you been to <u>I</u>taly?	☐	☐
6	Have you been t<u>o</u> Madrid?	☐	☐

b Listen again and check your answers.

Reading

Mae Jemison

This week we look at a real adventurer: Mae Jemison.

Mae has done many amazing things in her life, but perhaps the most amazing and important one is that she has been into space – she went on the space shuttle *Endeavour* in 1992. She was the first African-American woman astronaut. For this reason alone we can call Mae an adventurer, but she's done a lot more.

Mae was born in 1956 and when she was a child, she didn't know if she wanted to be a doctor or a dancer. She became a doctor, but she's also danced on stage and has produced several stage shows of modern jazz and African dance.

Mae has travelled all over the world: she went to Kenya, Cuba and Thailand during her studies to be a doctor in the late 1970s. She left university in 1981 and in 1983 she became a member of the

Peace Corps – that's an organisation for young American people to help people in poor countries. Mae worked in West Africa between 1983 and 1985 as a doctor. She has also worked as a general doctor in the United States and she joined NASA in 1987 and became an astronaut.

Not all of Mae's achievements are about hard work. She's written a book and she's also appeared in a television show – she was in an episode of *Star Trek* in 1993. She was the first real astronaut to appear in the show!

---

1 **a** Read the text quickly. Why is Mae Jemison famous?

1 She's danced and produced stage shows. ☐

2 She's appeared in *Star Trek*. ☐

3 She was the first African-American woman astronaut. ☐

b Read the text again and put the events from Mae's life in the correct order, 1–6.

a She went to Kenya and Cuba. ☐1☐

b She joined NASA. ☐

c She finished her studies. ☐

d She appeared in a TV show. ☐

e She went into space. ☐

f She joined the Peace Corps. ☐

2 Read the text again and decide if these statements are true (T) or false (F).

Mae hasn't travelled far. ☐F☐

1 Mae's first job was as a doctor. ☐

2 She went to West Africa during her studies. ☐

3 She became an astronaut when she left university. ☐

4 She's worked as an actor for a year. ☐

5 All the people in *Star Trek* are astronauts. ☐

6 She worked as a doctor in the US. ☐

7 She joined the Peace Corps to help poor people. ☐

8 She's appeared in a science fiction film. ☐

Grammar | Present Perfect: he/she/it

3 **a** Tick (✓) the things Mae has done. Cross (✗) the things she hasn't done.

She's ...

climbed a mountain.	✗

1 been into space. ☐
2 danced on stage. ☐
3 appeared on TV. ☐
4 sailed around the world. ☐
5 travelled to Africa. ☐
6 produced music and dance shows. ☐
7 worked in Australia. ☐

b Look at the sentences in exercise 3a and write questions and short answers.

Has Mae climbed a mountain?

No, she hasn't.

1 Has Mae been _____
_____

2 Has she _____
_____

3 _____
_____

4 _____
_____

5 _____
_____

6 _____
_____

7 _____
_____

4 **a** Write the past participles of these verbs.

drive *driven*

1 fly _____
2 ride _____
3 eat _____
4 meet _____
5 see _____

b Complete the sentences with the Present Perfect of the verbs in exercise 4a.

Have you ridden a horse?

1 I _____ in a hot-air balloon.
2 My parents _____ not _____ a 3D-film.
3 _____ you _____ my friend Aileen?
4 We _____ not _____ Japanese food.
5 My brother _____ a Ferrari.

5 Look at the table and write sentences in the Present Perfect.

	climb a mountain	run a marathon	cycle 50 km
Eddie	✓	✗	
Sue		✓	✗
Lyle	✗	✓	
Maria		✗	✓
Jack	✗		✓
Leila	✓		✗

Eddie *has climbed a mountain, but he hasn't run a marathon.*

1 Sue _____
_____

2 Lyle _____
_____

3 Maria _____
_____

4 Jack _____
_____

5 Leila _____
_____

Vocabulary | activities

6 Use the correct form of a verb from Box A and a phrase from Box B to complete the sentences.

Box A (climb   cross   fly   row   ~~sail~~)

Box B (a small aircraft   a small boat
~~across the Atlantic~~   Mount Everest
the Sahara Desert)

In 1985, my uncle *sailed across the Atlantic* in a boat.

1 These days a lot of people _____ and leave a lot of rubbish on the mountain!
2 The Wright brothers were the first people to _____ with an engine. They were in the air for twelve seconds.
3 We lived near a big lake when I was a child, so I learnt to _____ when I was very young.
4 My brother once did the Paris to Dakar car rally. He _____ from Tunis to Senegal.

Pronunciation | long and short vowels

7 **a** Underline the word with the long vowel in each pair.

a cat   **b** <u>car</u>
1 a fill   b feel
2 a taught   b top
3 a am   b arm
4 a heart   b hat
5 a cost   b course

b 🔵 33 Listen and check your answers. Then say the words.

Reading

1 a Read the text quickly and tick (✓) the correct box.

The notice gives:

1 information and advice ☐
2 information and rules ☐
3 advice ☐

b Match the <u>underlined</u> words in the text with the pictures.

①

sharp objects

②

_____

③

_____

④

_____

c Match the words from the text with their meanings.

1 proof
2 the hold
3 hand luggage
4 checked luggage
5 boarding
6 turn off

a The bags you give in at the check-in desk.
b Entering a plane.
c This is the place on a plane where they put the bags.
d Make a machine stop working.
e This shows that something is true.
f Small bags you take on the plane.

 Sunshine Holidays

If you are flying with *Go Faster Airlines* please read this notice before you go to the airport.

Documents

Go Faster Airlines uses an electronic check-in system. You don't have to bring your tickets to the check-in desk, but you have to bring proof of your identity (including your photo), for example a passport, driving licence or identity card. If you are flying to another country, you have to show your passport.

Luggage

With *Go Faster Airlines* you can check in a maximum of 20 kg of <u>luggage</u> to put in the hold. You can take a maximum of 5 kg of hand luggage. You can't put <u>sharp objects</u> in your hand luggage – you have to put them in your checked luggage. Your suitcase has to have a label with your name and address. The label doesn't have to have your flight number because that is on the electronic label.

Electronic devices

You have to turn off all <u>electronic devices</u> before boarding the plane. You can't use your mobile phone inside the plane.

Grammar | *can/can't, have to/don't have to*

2 Read the text in exercise 1 again. Tick (✓) the correct columns in the table.

	Necessary	Not necessary	Possible	Not possible
bring tickets to the check-in desk		✓		
1 bring proof of your identity				
2 show your passport when you fly to another country				
3 check in 20 kg of luggage				
4 take more than 5 kg of hand luggage				
5 put sharp objects in your hand luggage				
6 put a label on your suitcase with your name and address				
7 put your flight number on your suitcase label				
8 switch off electronic devices before you board the plane				
9 use a mobile phone inside the plane				

3 Look at the airport rules and write sentences with *can't* and *have to*.

> ### Rules
> - Be at check-in two hours before your departure time.
> - ~~No smoking on the plane.~~
> - Don't take drinks onto the plane.
> - Turn off your mobile phone before you board the plane.
> - Don't take food onto the plane.
> - Wear your seat belt during the flight.

can't

You can't smoke on the plane.

1 _____
_____

2 _____
_____

have to

3 _____
_____

4 _____
_____

5 _____
_____

4 Complete the sentences. Use *can/can't* or the correct form of *have to*.

It isn't necessary to wear a suit in my office.
I don't have to wear a suit in my office.

In New York people aren't allowed to smoke in restaurants.
In New York people can't smoke in restaurants.

1 It isn't possible to drive a car when you are only fifteen years old.
You _____
_____ .

2 Bring a friend to the party if you want to.
I _____
_____ .

3 In my office it isn't possible to use our mobile phones.
We _____
_____ .

4 Show your receipt to the manager.
You _____
_____ .

5 There isn't parking near the theatre.
You _____
_____ .

6 It isn't necessary for Amanda to pay because she's a member of the club.
Amanda _____
_____ .

7 We accept payment in cash or by credit card.
You _____
_____ .

8 It isn't necessary for David and Lucy to get visas to go to Canada.
David and Lucy _____
_____ .

5 All these statements give false information. Change the underlined verbs so the statements are true.

In most countries you <u>have to</u> get married when you are sixteen. *can*

1 You <u>can</u> take a gun on a plane. _____

2 You <u>can't</u> open a bank account when you are eighteen. _____

3 You <u>don't have to</u> have a passport or an identity card when your travel to foreign countries.
_____

4 You <u>have to</u> smoke in hospitals. _____

5 Men in the army usually <u>don't have to</u> have short hair. _____

6 In most countries you <u>don't have to</u> be eighteen to vote. _____

7 You <u>can't</u> usually pay by credit card in shops and restaurants. _____

8 In the US you <u>don't have to</u> drive on the right side of the road. _____

Pronunciation | /f/ and /v/

6 a 🔘 34 Listen and underline one more /f/ sound and one more /v/ sound in the sentence. Write the sound above them.

　　　　　　　　 /f/　　/v/
You don't have to have a French visa.

b 🔘 35 Listen and tick (✓) the correct box.

	/f/	/v/
I ha<u>v</u>e to go home now.	✓	☐
1 Do you ha<u>v</u>e a car?	☐	☐
2 I'<u>v</u>e got a question.	☐	☐
3 Let's ha<u>v</u>e a drink tomorrow.	☐	☐
4 Do you ha<u>v</u>e to leave now?	☐	☐

Reading

1 Read the interview quickly and match the people with their jobs.

1	Alana	a	Scottish hairdresser
2	Polly	b	English teacher
3	Neil	c	American scientist

2 **a** Read the interview again. Write *A* for Alana, *P* for Polly or *N* for Neil.

Which person...

	liked history and art?	N
1	left school quite early?	☐
2	didn't go to university?	☐
3	enjoyed sciences at school?	☐
4	went to college after university?	☐

b Complete the table with information from the interview.

		Polly	Alana	Neil
1	age started school	4		
2	location of school		Texas	
3	time spent at school			14 yrs
4	studied a language?			
5	favourite subject(s)			
6	went to university?			

In this month's *Clapton College coffee morning* we talk to three students on our Chinese evening course.

CC: Alana is from the United States.
Alana: That's right – Texas.
CC: Have you studied a language before?
Alana: No, I studied biology at university. I'm a scientist.
CC: Did you go to university in Texas?
Alana: No, I went to school in Texas, but university in New York.
CC: Polly, have you studied a language before?
Polly: No. Well, only French at secondary school in Glasgow, Scotland, but I left school at sixteen and went to technical college.
CC: What did you study at college?
Polly: Hairdressing, one day a week – I didn't want to spend any more time studying after twelve years at school!
Alana: So, when did you start school?
Neil: It's usually about four here. I was nearly five when I started school.
Alana: Wow! We usually start elementary school at about six in the States. Four seems very young!
Neil: Mm, it is. I left at eighteen, so I spent fourteen years at school here in London.
CC: Have you studied a language before?
Neil: Yes, I studied Spanish at university, just for a year.
CC: Where did you go to university?
Neil: London, then teacher training college.
CC: What do you teach?
Neil: History and art. They were my favourite subjects at school.
CC: What was your favourite subject, Alana? Biology?
Alana: No, I found it really difficult. But I liked the other science subjects – you know, physics and chemistry. And biology goes with them.
CC: How about you, Polly?
Polly: My favourite subject? Maybe English. I quite enjoyed that.
CC: Now, can we talk about your course here and your experiences ...

Vocabulary | schools and subjects

3 **a** Look at the interview on page 72. <u>Underline</u> the types of school/college and (circle) the subjects.

b Look at the interview again. Find:

1 four languages
Chinese, _____

2 three places to study after school
_____

3 three science subjects
_____

4 the school you start at six in the US
_____

Grammar | review of *wh-* questions

4 Complete these questions from the interview on page 72.

What *did* you *study* at college?

1 _____ did you _____ school?

2 _____ you go to university?

3 _____ you teach?

4 _____ was your _____ subject?

5 **a** Complete each group of questions with a word/phrase from the box.

> how   how many   what   when   where
> ~~which~~   who

Which subjects did you do?
school did you go to?
teacher do you like best?

1 _____ students are there in your class?
languages can you speak?
subjects have you got on Monday?

2 _____ do you sit next to?
is your favourite film star?
do you live with?

3 _____ is the school?
is your house?
do you go in the evenings?

4 _____ time is it?
do you do at the weekend?
did you watch on TV yesterday?

5 _____ do you get to the school?
do you spend your holidays?
did you find this school?

6 _____ do you get up?
did you start learning English?
do you take exercise?

b Write a question from exercise 5a for each answer.

1 *Which school did you go to?*
I went to Kingston High School.

2 _____
We often go to a bar or to the cinema.

3 _____
Two years ago.

4 _____
My parents and my younger brother.

5 _____
I take the bus.

6 _____
A programme about the Sahara desert.

7 _____
Three – physics, maths and English.

c Look at the questions in exercise 5b. Write answers that are true for you.

1 _____
2 _____
3 _____
4 _____
5 _____
6 _____
7 _____

Pronunciation | intonation of *wh-* questions

6 **a** ◉ 36 Look at the questions in exercise 4. Does the voice go up or down in the questions? Listen and write ⬈ or ⬊ by each question.

What did you study at college? ⬊

b Now repeat the questions.

Vocabulary | new technology

7 Complete the text with words from the box.

> download   forum   ~~online~~   podcasts   posts

How do people go through a day without computers now? I spend part of each day on my laptop. I go *online* at least twice a day to read my emails or (1) _____ music. Then I often listen to (2) _____ if there's anything interesting on the BBC. Most days I go into my university website and go onto the class (3) _____ to see if there are any new (4) _____ . We have a class wiki, too, but not many people use that – I think a lot of us aren't sure what to do!

Vocabulary | education

1 Complete the table with words from the box.

> academic distance learning courses evening classes
> full-time lecturer part-time professional
> student trainee trainer tutor well-qualified

Adjectives	Types of education	People learning	People teaching
academic			

2 Choose the correct words in *italics*.

Luke studied for a year to become a fitness *trainer/trainee* in a famous gym.

1 I want to be an architect, so I'm taking *an academic/ a professional* qualification after I finish university.

2 I can't afford to stop working, so I'm taking a *full-time/part-time* course two evenings a week.

3 The classes at our college are very good – there are usually only about ten *tutors/students* in them.

4 I enjoy studying at home on my own, so *an evening class/a distance learning course* is very good for me.

5 Professor Simmonds is a very good *lecturer/trainer* – whenever she gives a talk in the main hall, about 200 students come to it.

Listening

3 **a** ● 37 Listen to a phone call between a student and a secretary at his university. What does the student want to do?

1 see his tutor

2 start a new course

3 go to a workshop

b Listen again and answer the questions.

Which department is Tariq in?

Media studies.

1 When are the photography workshops?

_____

2 Can Tariq book a workshop over the phone?

_____

3 Who is Tariq's tutor?

_____

4 **a** Look at the information below. Then listen again and complete Tariq's note to his tutor.

Tariq has an interview next Wednesday. He prefers afternoons because he lives a long way from the university.

> Dear Ms Adams,
>
> Here is the information you need for the photography workshop:
>
> Name: (1) _____
> Student number: (2) _____
> 1st choice: Thursday afternoon
> 2nd choice: (3) _____
> Can't come on: (4) _____
>
> T. Raschid

b What does the secretary tell Tariq to do with his note? Tick (✓) the correct picture.

Secretary: Media studies department. Can I help you?

Tariq: Hello, yes, er... I'm a student in your department. I think there's a photography workshop next week. Do I have to book a place on it?

Secretary: Yes, you do. What's your name, please?

Tariq: Tariq, Tariq Raschid.

Secretary: One moment. Oh yes, student number AX327. Is that right?

Tariq: Yes.

Secretary: OK. There's a message on your forum about booking for the workshop.

Tariq: Sorry, I haven't looked at the forum for a few days. Can I book now?

Secretary: No, not with me. You have to book through your tutor, but it's quite easy. There are four workshops. They're all next week – Wednesday morning, Wednesday afternoon, Thursday morning and Thursday afternoon. Write your tutor a note with your first and second choices of day and time. And be sure to write down if you can't come on one of the days. Then write your name and student number and sign it. OK?

Tariq: Yes, I think so. I write my name and student number, my first choice and second choice for the workshops and then I sign it and send it to my tutor. Is that right?

Secretary: Well, the tutors are preparing the lists for the workshops now, so email it – it's faster.

Tariq: I'm actually in the university now, so can I just give it to my tutor?

Secretary: OK, who's your tutor?

Tariq: Bryony Addams.

Secretary: Just a moment. Right, Ms Addams is giving a tutorial in her office at the moment. Take the note with your choices to her, but don't go into her room. Just put it under the door.

Tariq: OK. She's in room fourteen, isn't she?

Secretary: Yes, that's right.

Grammar | the imperative

5 Put the words in the correct order to make imperative sentences.

put   the post   the letter   don't   in
Don't put the letter in the post.

1 your shoes   the door   outside   leave

_____

2 your name   write   every page   at the top of

_____

3 faster than   don't   50 kph   on this road   drive

_____

4 with   the form   complete   a black pen

_____

6 Write imperatives for each of these pictures. Use the prompts to help you.

buy/tickets/here
Buy your tickets here.

park/here

_____

put/it/in the washing machine

_____

please/take/your rubbish/home

_____

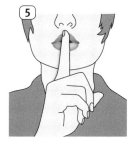

talk/in the library

_____

play/ball/on the grass

_____

Reading

1 **a** Read the postcard and answer the questions.

Is Daniela Anthony's girlfriend or his sister?

His sister.

1 Where is Daniela's hotel?

_____

2 Where did they sunbathe?

_____

3 When are they going to the hills?

_____

b Complete the postcard with words and phrases from the box.

> canyon ~~coast~~ island sailing trekking
> white-water rafting

Dear Anthony

We're having a fantastic holiday! Our hotel
is near the <u>coast</u> – it's just a few hundred
metres to the sea. There are lots of activities
here. Last Wednesday we went (1) _____
on the river. It was scary, but very exciting!
The river is at the bottom of a huge
(2) _____ . On Friday we went to a small
(3) _____ . There was a nice beach, so we
sunbathed in the morning and in the afternoon
we went (4) _____ on a beautiful old
boat. Tomorrow we're going (5) _____ in the
hills. I'm a bit nervous about that!

Love
Daniela

Listening

2 **a** 🔵 38 Listen to Anthony and Belinda talking. What is the connection between the photo and the map?

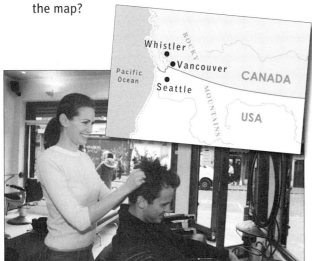

b Listen again and put Anthony's plans in the correct order, 1–7.

a go trekking in the Rocky Mountains ☐

b stay in Seattle ☐

c fly home ☐

d drive to the American border ☐

e stay with his cousins ☐

f fly to Vancouver 1

g go to Whistler ☐

c Choose the correct words in *italics*.

Anthony is going to stay with his *girlfriend*/(cousins) in Vancouver.

1 Anthony and his cousins are going to go *mountain climbing*/*trekking*.

2 He's going to *drive*/*fly* to Seattle.

3 Anthony's girlfriend *is*/*isn't* a teacher.

4 Anthony and his girlfriend are going to stay in Seattle for *two weeks*/*ten days*.

Grammar | *be going to*

3 **a** Complete the audioscript with the correct form of *be going to*.

B: So, what are you going to do this summer?

A: Well, I haven't got my tickets yet, but I'm planning to go to Canada. I**'m going to** visit my cousins in Vancouver.

B: Really? That sounds exciting!

A: Yes. I haven't been to Canada before.

B: People say it's beautiful. (1) _____ you _____ travel around or stay in one place?

A: Well, I think I (2) _____ fly to Vancouver and stay with my cousins first. Then they (3) _____ take me to Whistler in the mountains.

B: Mountain climbing?

A: No, we (4) _____ go trekking. We (5) _____ spend three weeks trekking around the Rocky Mountains. Then I (6) _____ drive down to the American border. I want to see Seattle.

B: (7) _____ your girlfriend _____ travel with you?

A: Well, she isn't a teacher like me, so she can only take two weeks' holiday. She (8) _____ join me in Seattle. We (9) _____ stay there for ten days and then we (10) _____ fly back together at the beginning of September.

B: You're lucky. It sounds wonderful!

b Listen again and check your answers.

4 Write sentences. Use *be going to* and the words in brackets.

We stayed with our uncle last week.
(visit our cousins/next month)
We're going to visit our cousins next month.

She didn't buy any pasta at the shops.
(not cook lasagne/this evening)
She isn't going to cook lasagne this evening.

1 I started the course in June.
(finish the course/in September)
_____

2 Did you write a letter to the travel agent?
(no/send an email/tomorrow)
_____

3 Last year they stayed with relatives in France.
(this year/stay with friends/in Spain)
_____

4 Henry went white-water rafting in Colorado last year. (go/sailing in Canada/next year)
_____

5 She didn't study physics at secondary school.
(not study science/at university)
_____

6 I didn't do any homework last night.
(but/study/this weekend)
_____

5 What are the people in the pictures thinking? Write a sentence for each picture. Use *be going to*.

We're going to buy a dishwasher.

Pronunciation | sentence stress, /ə/

6 **a** ⊙ 39 Listen and <u>underline</u> the stress in these sentences.

I'm <u>going</u> to join a <u>gym</u>.
1 He's going to fly to Rome.
2 We're going to buy a car.
3 I'm going to see the doctor.
4 She's going to meet my parents.
5 They're going to stay at home.
6 He's going to be a painter.

b Listen again and repeat, stressing the correct words. Be careful with the pronunciation of *to*.

Vocabulary | future time

7 Write the <u>underlined</u> time expressions in the correct order.

I'm going to finish the course <u>summer next</u>.
next summer

1 He's going to take his driving test <u>this later year</u>.
_____

2 We're going to take the children to Disneyland <u>the next week after</u>. _____

3 <u>In years' three time</u> I'm going to be a doctor!
_____

4 Are you going to have a holiday <u>year next</u>?
_____

5 They're going to open the new tunnel <u>years four now from</u>. _____

6 I'm going to open a new bank account <u>tomorrow after the day</u>. _____

7 Our grandparents are going to visit us in <u>time weeks' two</u>. _____

Reading

Today's news and gossip

1

Beautiful Karina Burton, singer with Girl Power, is leaving the band to start a new career. After eleven years and many hit songs, Karina is going to begin a new life as a solo singer. On her Twitter website Karina wrote, 'It was not my choice to leave, but it's time to try something new in my life.' We're sure the talented singing star is going to have a lot of success in the future!

2

Pop superstar Madonna is going to direct a movie about Wallis Simpson, an American woman who wanted to marry the king of England in the 1930s. The singer has directed a movie before, but of course she is more famous for her music. Madonna came to London last week to talk to actors Cate Blanchett and David Tennant about parts in the film. Madonna isn't going to act in the movie, but it is going to be a musical.

3

Nigel Page and Justine Laycock from Cirencester, Gloucestershire won £56 million in the Euromillions lottery. They are Britain's biggest winners. They are using some of their new fortune to buy a huge £4 million house and a BMW. But they've also remembered their cleaner, Denise Kelso. Friends of the couple tell us they're going to give the cleaner their old house and their Honda Civic! Lucky Denise!

1 **a** Read the text quickly. Match the headings (a–c) with paragraphs 1–3.

a Singer's new film ☐ c Girl Power shock! ☐

b Generous lottery winners! ☐

b Read the text again and answer the questions.

How many years was Karina Burton in Girl Power?

Eleven.

1 What website does Karina use?

_____

2 What has Madonna done before?

_____

3 Who was Wallis Simpson?

_____

4 How much money did Nigel and Justine win in the lottery?

_____

5 Who is Denise Kelso?

_____

c Complete the summaries of the paragraphs in the text. Use one word in each gap.

1 Karina Burton is *going* to begin a new career as a solo singer. She was in _____ Power for eleven years.

2 Madonna is in _____ to talk to some actors about her new film. The film is going to be a _____ about Wallis Simpson.

3 Nigel Page and Justine Laycock won £56 _____ in the Euromillions lottery. They _____ going to give their old house to their _____ , Denise Kelso.

Pronunciation | rhymes

2 Make pairs of rhyming words. Use words from the box.

> alone   blue   clever   cold   ~~cry~~   free   mine   name
> nice   shows

	fly	_cry_			do	_____
1	price	_____	5	do	_____
2	knows	_____	6	forever	_____
3	fame	_____	7	fine	_____
4	hold	_____	8	see	_____
			9	home	_____

3 Complete the poem with words from exercise 2.

When I'm at home
Or feeling _alone_,
When I feel blue,
Or there's nothing to (1) _____ ,
When I'm cold,
Or need someone to (2) _____ ,
It's always the same.
I think of your (3) _____ .
And then I feel fine,
Because I know that you're (4) _____ .

Grammar | infinitive of purpose

4 Match 1–6 with a–f to make sentences. Then write the sentences below.

Action	Purpose
1 I'm going to start a part-time computing course	a get fit
	b visit our grandparents
2 You can use a computer	c send emails
3 She's joining a gym	d learn all about web design
4 Mike uses his bicycle	e get a better job
5 We went to Warsaw	f commute to work
6 I'm going to improve my English	

1 _I'm going to start a part-time computing course to learn all about web design._

2 _____

3 _____

4 _____

5 _____

6 _____

5 Put the words in the correct order to make sentences. Add _to_ in the correct place.

sunbathe   the beach   I   go to

I go to the beach to sunbathe.

1 Jane   her boyfriend   Berlin   flew to   visit

_____
_____

2 play   my son   his computer   uses   games

_____
_____

3 an MP3 player   music   listen to   I'm going to get

_____
_____

4 we   food   always   buy   fresh   go to   the market

_____
_____

5 see   went to   my brother   the Hermitage Museum   St Petersburg

_____
_____

6 **a** Find and underline the mistakes. Then correct them.

Karina Burton is leaving Girl Power <u>for start</u> a new career as a solo singer.
to start

1 Madonna came to London last week talk to actors Cate Blanchett and David Tennant about parts in her new film. _____

2 Nigel Page and Justine Laycock are using some of their new fortune to buying a £4 million mansion and a BMW. _____

b Now look at the text on page 78 and check your answers.

Listening

1 **a** 🔘 40 Cover the audioscript. Listen to a dialogue between four friends. Tick (✓) the four ambitions they talk about.

1 be an accountant ☐
2 go around the world ☐
3 work for a charity ☐
4 win a lot of money ☐
5 be a rock singer ☐
6 be a businesswoman ☐

b Listen again and complete the sentences.

Alex would like to *win a lot of money and retire.*

1 Matt would like to _____
   _____ .

2 Dee would like to _____
   _____ .

3 Jamie would like to _____
   _____ .

Grammar | *like* and *would like*

2 Complete the sentences. Then listen again or look at the audioscript to check your answers.

1 Alex wants to do something different. She'd like *to win* a lot of money and retire, but she doesn't like _____ all day.

2 Matt would like _____ around the world, but he doesn't like _____ .

3 Dee would like _____ a charity and help people.

4 Jamie _____ charity work because it isn't very well-paid. He would really like _____ a rock singer – he loves _____ the guitar and he likes _____ .

AUDIOSCRIPT

Jamie: What's wrong, Alex? You look bored today.

Alex: I am. Well, I'm not bored right now, but I'm really bored with my job. It's the same thing every day. I really want to do something different.

Jamie: Like what? Find another job?

Alex: Well, I don't know. I suppose I'd like to win a lot of money and retire!

Dee: Come on, Alex, I know you. You don't like doing nothing. You love being busy.

Alex: Mm, maybe. But you have to think about getting away sometimes.

Matt: Yes, that's right. I'd like to fly around the world and see lots of interesting places.

Dee: You, Matt? But you hate flying! You're not going to get on a long-haul flight!

Matt: I hate flying, but I love going to new places. Anyway, don't you ever want to change your life, Dee?

Dee: Me? Yes, of course. I'd like to do something different – something that helps people. I don't know, maybe work for a charity or something.

Jamie: Dee, you're a successful businesswoman. You wouldn't like charity work. It isn't really a challenge for you. I wouldn't like to do it. It isn't very well-paid.

Dee: Money isn't important.

Jamie: You know what I'd really like to be?

Matt: No.

Jamie: A rock singer.

Alex: Really? But you play the guitar, Jamie.

Jamie: I know, and I love playing the guitar. But I enjoy singing, too, and I'm having singing lessons at the moment.

Matt: I didn't know that.

Jamie: Mm, and I'm in a new rock band – we play in clubs at the weekend now and people like us.

Dee: So what about your job?

Jamie: My job as an accountant? I'm going to do it for another year or so, but the band is making a CD later this year, so …

Dee: Wow, Jamie! You're going to be famous!

3 **a** Find six more mistakes and <u>underline</u> them.

As you know, I left my job last month. I worked in an office and I really <u>didn't like be</u> inside all the time. Now I have to find another job. I wouldn't like working in an office again, so I'm thinking about some more training. I really love to do water sports and I would like to becoming a water sports teacher. It's a good job here as there are a lot of tourists in the summer and most of them like learn waterskiing or windsurfing. I've had an interview to train as a teacher, but there's a problem. Part of the exam is written and I really don't like to take written exams – I always do very badly. I really like starting training in March. Then I can start teaching in the summer. Can you suggest any ways of helping me study for the exam?

b Now correct the mistakes in exercise 3a.

didn't like being

1 _____
2 _____
3 _____
4 _____
5 _____
6 _____

4 What do these people want to do with their lives? Why? Write sentences. Use words and phrases from the box.

> be with children   drive fast   help young people
> listen to music   visit different countries
> ~~work in the garden~~

1

large garden

He would like to have a large garden because he likes working in the garden.

2

racing driver

_____
_____
_____

3

good music system

_____
_____
_____

4

teacher

_____
_____
_____
_____

5

holiday rep

_____
_____
_____
_____

6

lots of grandchildren

_____
_____
_____
_____

5 Write one sentence about your likes and ambitions for each of these topics.

work and study

I really like watching films, so I'd like to do an evening course in film history.

1 work and study

_____
_____

2 marriage and children

_____
_____

3 travel and holidays

_____
_____

4 sport

_____
_____

Pronunciation | /aɪ/ and /eɪ/

6 🔵 41 Listen to the words and write them in pairs in the table. The main difference between the words in each pair is the vowel sound (/aɪ/ or /eɪ/).

> ~~day~~   ~~die~~   mine   size   light   hate   late
> wait   height   main   say   white   try   train

/aɪ/	/eɪ/
die	*day*

Grammar
-ing form as noun

1 Tick (✓) the correct sentences and cross (✗) the incorrect sentences. Then <u>underline</u> the mistakes and correct them.

I think waiting for a bus is boring.   ✓

<u>Cycle</u> is popular in Amsterdam.   ✗   *Cycling*

1   These days fly is very popular.   ☐ _____

2   In London going to the cinema are expensive.   ☐ _____

3   Swimming is very relaxing.   ☐ _____

4   On the Internet pay by credit card is easy.   ☐ _____

5   Sunbathing are bad for your skin.   ☐ _____

6   I think skiing in the mountains is fantastic!   ☐ _____

Present Perfect

2 Complete the questions and answers with the correct form of *have*. Use contracted forms where possible.

1   A: Have you <u>been</u> to England?
     B: No, I _____ been there.

2   A: _____ your father been on a long-haul flight?
     B: Yes, he _____ .

3   A: _____ you been to a rock concert?
     B: No, I _____ .

4   A: _____ your wife been to South America?
     B: Yes, she _____ been to Argentina and Chile.

5   A: _____ you been on an adventure holiday?
     B: Yes, we _____ been bungee jumping in France.

3 Make questions and negative sentences in the Present Perfect.

she/see/an opera (?)

Has she seen an opera?

I/go/to a zoo (✗)

I haven't been to a zoo.

1   I/drive/a sports car (✗)

_____

2   you/take/the driving test (?)

_____

3   she/go/to New York (?)

_____

4   I/see/that film (✗)

_____

5   we/visit/Australia (✗)

_____

6   you/fly/in a helicopter (?)

_____

7   Lena/climb/a mountain (?)

_____

8   we/go/horse riding (✗)

_____

The imperative, *can/can't* and *have to/don't have to*

4 a Complete the notice with verbs from the box.

> bring   don't bring   ~~don't smoke~~   don't use
> show

Brindsley College
INFORMATION FOR STUDENTS

1   • *Don't smoke* in the college building.
2   (Smoking is possible in the garden.)
3   • (a) _____ food or drinks into the classrooms.
4   (It is possible to get coffee and tea in the college café.)
5   • (b) _____ an identity card when you come into the college.
6   • (c) _____ mobile phones during lessons.
7   • Using the computers in the library is possible in the evenings.
8   (It isn't necessary to pay to use the computers.)
9   • (d) _____ a pen and some paper to lessons.
10   (But it isn't necessary to bring a dictionary.)

b Rewrite the numbered sentences from the notice in exercise 4a. Use *can/can't* or *have to/ don't have to*.

1   *You can't smoke in the college building.*
2   _____
3   _____
4   _____
5   _____
6   _____
7   _____
8   _____
9   _____
10   _____

be going to

5 Complete the text. Use *be going to* and the verbs in brackets.

From: Erik
To: Hilary

Hi Hilary

Thanks for your last letter. Congratulations on your new job! Things are very busy for us at the moment. We moved into our new house last week. It's very old and there are a lot of things we want to do. We *'re going to build* (build) a new kitchen because the old one is really small. My brother-in-law (1) _____ (do) the work because he's a builder. We (2) _____ (not/buy) the equipment from the local shops – they're very expensive! Amanda (3) _____ (buy) all the equipment from the Internet! I think she (4) _____ (get) one of those huge American fridges! We both love cooking, so we (5) _____ (have) a really good cooker, but Amanda (6) _____ (not/get) a microwave because she hates microwaved food! We also want to do things in the garden. I (7) _____ (buy) lots of beautiful new plants.

How are things with you? What's your new job like? (8) _____ (you/stay) there for a long time? Send me an email and let me know your plans. (9) _____ (you/visit) us soon?

Love
Erik

Infinitive of purpose

6 Put the words in the correct order to make sentences.

the gym   go to   get   I   to   fit
I go to the gym to get fit.

1 to send   her phone   Jo   uses   emails

_____

2 some eggs   went to   buy   Christine   to   the supermarket

_____

3 my iPod   music   I   listen to   use   to

_____

4 a club   joined   new people   Ali   to meet

_____

5 meet   went to   friends   to   the park   I   my

_____

like and would like

7 Choose the correct words in *italics*.

Clara doesn't like *sunbathe/sunbathing*, so she never goes to the beach.

1 I *like/'d like* to go to China next summer.
2 Johan loves *play/playing* football and he would like *to be/being* a professional footballer.
3 We love *to garden/gardening*, so we *wouldn't like/don't like* to live in an apartment.
4 I never go to classical concerts because I don't like *listen/listening* to classical music.
5 We'd like to *come/coming* to your party next week, but we're really busy.
6 I usually cook because my husband *doesn't/wouldn't* like doing it.
7 They're studying English because they'd like *to get/getting* better jobs.
8 My girlfriend loves *go/going* to the cinema, but she *doesn't/wouldn't* like watching TV.

Vocabulary

8 Complete the sentences with words from units 10–12. The first letter of each word is there.

I use a computer and the Internet and do most of my work o*nline*.

1 Do you d_____ music from the Internet?
2 A p_____ school is a school for young children.
3 A t_____ is a university teacher.
4 I use an Internet f_____ to ask questions and get answers.
5 Deborah wants to be famous, so she's entering a t_____ show on TV.
6 After you pass the driving test, you get a driving l_____ .
7 A c_____ is an organisation that helps people.

9 Match 1–8 with a–h.

1 distance   a climbing
2 talent   b learning
3 return   c jumping
4 bungee   d ticket
5 mountain   e lights
6 rush   f rafting
7 white water   g show
8 traffic   h hour

Answer key

Unit 1

Lesson 1.1

1a
AUSTRALIA ARGENTINA RUSSIA SPAIN ITALY BRAZIL
The letter in the centre is I.

1b
1 BRAZILIAN 2 AUSTRALIAN 3 JAPANESE 4 POLISH 5 SPANISH
6 AMERICAN 7 CHINESE 8 ITALIAN 9 ENGLISH 10 (across) GERMAN
10 (down) GREEK 11 CZECH

2
1 Russian 2 German 3 Japanese 4 American 5 Chinese 6 Polish

3
1 we are 2 I am 3 he is 4 they are 5 you are 6 it is

4
1 are am 2 is are 3 be are 4 am is 5 are is

5
2 d B 3 a D 4 c A

6
1 from 2 American 3 is 4 He's 5 Russia 6 Where 7 She's 8 German

7
1 is he from 2 are they from 3 is it 4 is she 5 are you from 6 are they
7 is she from

8a
1 What's 2 is 3 Italian 4 John and Liz 5 What's 6 Canadian

8b
Montreal: Jean Pierre
São Paolo: Elda
London: John and Liz
Warsaw: Misha
Rimini: Claudio

Lesson 1.2

1a
1 Manuel 2 Marta 3 Pedro

1b
1 Marta's and Pedro's 2 Manuel's 3 husband 4 niece 5 children 6 son
7 Cecilia's 8 grandfather 9 Eduardo

2a
1 Marianne's 2 Maria's 3 Rafael's 4 Karin's 5 Jane's 6 Anna's
7 Paulo's 8 Connor's 9 Nicole's 10 Amy's

2b
1 Stefan is Ana's brother.
2 Giorgio and Sophia are Mario's parents.
3 Clara is Mr and Mrs Moreno's daughter.
4 Vanessa is Dieter's sister.
5 Alejandro and Elena are Manu's children.
6 Victor and Serge are Halyna's sons.
7 Stephanie is Pierre's niece.
8 José is Isabel's father-in-law.

3
1 he his 2 she her 3 I my 4 we our 5 you your

4a
They are in an airport.

4b
1 woman 2 man 3 man 4 woman

4c
1 his watch 2 their bag 3 her mobile phone 4 his jacket

5
2 e 3 f 4 a 5 b 6 c

6
1 They're from Greece. 2 His name is John.
3 No, he isn't. He's from Australia. 4 They're from the United States.
5 It's in Sydney. 6 Yes, she is.

Lesson 1.3

1
2 dentist 3 shop assistant 4 computer programmer 5 engineer 6 chef

2
1 actor 2 TV producer 3 lawyer 4 architect 5 doctor

3
1 a 2 an 3 an 4 A, an 5 a 6 a

4
Students' own answers.

5
1 an doctor a doctor 2 a retired retired 3 architect an architect
4 an unemployed unemployed 5 lawyer a lawyer 6 an chef a chef

7a
1 My address is 20 Cedar Drive. 2 My grandparents are retired.
3 My young cousin is beautiful. 4 Esther's from Colombia.
5 My nephew's a doctor. 6 My parents are Greek. 7 They're friends.

7b
1 My address isn't 20 Cedar Drive. 2 My grandparents aren't retired.
3 My young cousin isn't beautiful. 4 Esther isn't from Colombia.
5 My nephew isn't a doctor. 6 My parents aren't Greek.
7 They aren't friends.

8a
names: Martin, Daniel, Bernadette, Nicole, Francis, Heather
jobs: police officer, lawyer, teacher, model, photographer, assistant

8b
2 d ii 3 e iv 4 c iii 5 a vi 6 f v

9
1 No, he isn't called Steve. He's called Martin.
2 No, she isn't English. She's French.
3 No, they aren't in London. They're in Paris.
4 No, she isn't a lawyer. She's a teacher.
5 No, they aren't teachers. Her brother's a photographer/student and
   her sister's a model.

Unit 2

Lesson 2.1

1a
2

1b
1 have breakfast 2 talk to my assistant
3 have coffee (with the holiday reps) and talk about the clients
4 watch TV

2a
1 I have a wash. 2 I go to work at nine o'clock.
3 I check the hotel rooms and the swimming pool.
4 I have lunch in the hotel restaurant. 5 I have lunch at one o'clock.
6 I have dinner and watch TV. 7 I watch TV at ten o'clock.
8 I go to bed at half past eleven.

2b
1 No, I don't. 2 Yes, I am. 3 Yes, I do. 4 Yes, I do. 5 No, I don't.
6 Yes, I am. 7 No, I don't.

2c
Students' own answers.

3
1 meet 2 have 3 get up 4 restaurant 5 holiday rep 6 have 7 finish
8 play 9 guests 10 nightclub

4

1 do you do 2 don't 3 Do 4 do you go 5 Do you work 6 do you finish
7 meet 8 go

5

1 Where do you work? 2 Are you a doctor?
3 When/What time do you go to work?
4 Do you have lunch in the hospital?
5 When/What time do you leave work?
6 What do you do/Where do you go in the evening?

6

1 ✓ 2 ✓ 3 <u>Get up you</u> Do you get up 4 ✓ 5 <u>you go</u> do you go
6 ✓ 7 <u>you do leave</u> do you leave 8 ✓ 9 ✓ 10 <u>don't</u> I don't
11 ✓ 12 <u>work</u> do

Lesson 2.2

1a

1 an electrical shop 2 bus 3 5:30

1b

7:15	He has breakfast.
7:45	He leaves home.
8:30	(The shop opens and) he starts work.
12:30	He has lunch.
5:30	He leaves work.
7:00	He has dinner.
11:00	He goes to bed.

2

have, wash, have, leave, walk, wait, opens, start, work, sell, like, talk,
have, leave, play, have, watch, listen, go

3a

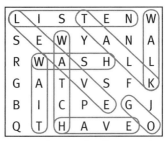

In any order: 1 wash 2 have 3 wait 4 watch 5 walk 6 leave 7 talk
8 go

3b

1 have 2 leave 3 talk 4 wash 5 go

4

A 3 wash hair B 5 read a newspaper C 1 have breakfast
D 4 cook dinner E 6 go to bed F 2 leave home

5

1 gets up 2 have 3 leaves 4 washes 5 dries 6 talk 7 watches
8 finishes 9 doesn't get 10 makes 11 go 12 reads 13 listens
14 doesn't watch

6

1 She doesn't leave home at quarter past eight. She leaves home at
  half past seven.
2 She doesn't watch the hairdressers in the afternoon. She watches
  the actors in the afternoon.
3 She doesn't finish work at half past six. She finishes work at half
  past four.
4 She doesn't make dinner for her friends. She makes dinner for her
  children.
5 She doesn't go to bed at about ten o'clock. She goes to bed at about
  eleven o'clock.

7a

1 Where does Melanie work?
2 Do Melanie's children have breakfast with her?
3 Does she wash her children's hair at work?
4 Do the actors talk to Melanie?
5 When does she finish work?
6 What time do the children go to bed?
7 What does Melanie do in the evening?
8 What time does she go to bed?

7b

1 She works in a film studio. 2 Yes, they do. 3 No, she doesn't.
4 Yes, they do. 5 She finishes work at half past four.
6 They go to bed at about half past eight.
7 She reads the newspaper or listens to music.
8 She goes to bed at about eleven o'clock.

8a

/z/: leaves, goes /s/: works, makes /ɪz/: watches, finishes

Lesson 2.3

1a

1 cameras 2 diaries 3 families 4 games 5 holidays 6 cars
7 scarves 8 suitcases 9 watches 10 wives

1b

1 have, holidays 2 want, cars 3 like, scarves 4 families, work
5 addresses, forms 6 use, diaries 7 play, games 8 wives, are
9 take, suitcases 10 are, watches

2a

1 big 2 horrible 3 old 4 pretty 5 useless 6 old-fashioned

2b

1 big 2 nice 3 old 4 pretty 5 useful 6 old-fashioned

3

1 down: green, 1 across: grey, 2 yellow 3 blue 4 black 5 brown 6 red
7 white

4a

2A, 3B, 4D

4b

2 That's an ugly belt! 3 These are (really) old-fashioned shoes!
4 Those are modern MP3 players.

5a

1 What are these? 2 What's that? 3 What are those?

6a

this: big, dictionary, Spanish, think, is
these: niece, green, people

Unit 3

Lesson 3.1

1

2 Joe, Tracy 3 Joe, Lynn

2a

Lynn

2b

1 always 2 sometimes 3 sometimes 4 occasionally 5 never

3a

1 Tracy always listens to music in the evening.
2 Lynn sometimes watches a DVD in the evening.
3 Lynn never goes to the gym in the evening.
4 Tracy occasionally goes to the cinema in the evening.
5 Tracy usually goes to the gym in the evening.
6 Lynn often goes for a walk in the evening.

3b

1 Joe never goes to the gym after work.
2 Joe always reads in bed.
3 Joe usually watches a DVD in the evening.
4 Joe often listens to music after dinner.
5 Joe always cooks at home.
6 Joe occasionally goes for a walk in the park.

4a

do: my shopping, our homework
go for: a walk
go: running
go on: the Internet
go to: the gym, a concert, an evening class, the cinema
have: a sandwich
read: a book

4b
1 has a sandwich 2 do our homework 3 go running
4 goes to an evening class 5 do my shopping 6 go for a walk
7 go to a concert 8 go to the cinema 9 go on the Internet
10 reads a book

5a
go running, go to an evening class

5b
Monday a.m. go swimming
Tuesday a.m. go to the gym
Wednesday a.m. go swimming
Thursday a.m. go to the gym; p.m. go to a concert
Friday a.m. go swimming; p.m. go on Facebook
Saturday a.m. go shopping; p.m. stay at home and relax
Sunday a.m. go for a walk on the beach; p.m. have lunch

Lesson 3.2

1a
2 D 3 G 4 A 5 E 6 B 7 J 8 C 9 H 10 F

1b
2 go skiing 3 go cycling 4 go windsurfing 5 do yoga 6 play chess
7 play basketball 8 go rowing 9 go running 10 play tennis

2a
1 tennis 2 dance 3 basketball 4 yoga 5 aerobics

2b
1 go dance go dancing 2 play aerobics do aerobics
3 do swimming go swimming 4 does games plays games
5 go judo do judo

3a
3

3b
2 a 3 d 4 e 5 f 6 b

4
1 can sing 2 can drive (racing cars) 3 can act
4 can make good films 5 can play football

5a
1 can 2 can 3 can't 4 can 5 Can 6 can 7 Can 8 can't 9 can 10 can't
11 can 12 can

5b
1 She can ride a bike and play tennis.
2 She can't teach judo, but she can teach aerobics.
3 She can't play the guitar.
4 She can speak German and Spanish, but she can't speak French.
5 She can drive.

6

	/æ/	/ə/	/ɑː/
1 Yes, I can.	✓		
2 Yes, I can sing …		✓	
3 I can't paint …			✓
4 … I can play tennis.		✓	
5 Can you teach … ?		✓	
6 I can teach aerobics.	✓		
7 Can you play the guitar?		✓	
8 No, I can't.			✓
9 Yes, I can speak German …		✓	
10 No, I can't speak French.			✓
11 And can you drive?		✓	
12 Yes, I can.	✓		

Lesson 3.3

1a
a 2 b 3 c 1

1b
1 432,400 2 55 3 738 4 35 5 22

2
1 432,400 four hundred and thirty-two thousand, four hundred
2 88 eighty-eight
3 55 fifty-five
4 738,000,000 seven hundred and thirty-eight (million)
5 35 thirty-five
6 20 twenty
7 10 ten
8 22 twenty-two

3
Students' own answers.

4a
1 forty 2 fifteen 3 fifty 4 eighty 5 eighteen

4b
1 a 2 b 3 b 4 b

5a
2 3 1

5b
1 Phone number: 09404 8832
2 Phone number: 0991 344562
   Message: She can't see you tomorrow. She can see you on Friday at
   7:10?
3 Phone number: 8947701
   Message: (Please) call him after 4:30.

6
1 take 2 ask 3 number 4 call

7
1 there here 2 make take 3 speak ask 4 What are What's 5 I am It's

Review and consolidation 1–3

1
1 She 2 We 3 They 4 I 5 It 6 you

2a
2 are 3 is 4 is 5 Are 6 Is 7 Is 8 Are 9 is 10 are
a isn't b 'm c 's d is e 's f aren't g 're h 's i 'm j 's

2b
2 i 3 c 4 e 5 b 6 d 7 a 8 f 9 h 10 g

3
1 Maria's, her 2 their 3 my 4 his 5 our 6 William's 7 our 8 my

4
1 sometimes works 2 never walks 3 does John usually have
4 occasionally goes 5 Does Susan always wash 6 don't go
7 doesn't live 8 're often

5
1 Does he often stay in a hotel?
2 Do you have a break at lunchtime?
3 Do your parents have a holiday every year?
4 Do you work in an office?
5 Is he a student?
6 Do they have an unemployed son?
7 Does she work in a famous restaurant?
8 Do you have an iPod?

6
1 C 2 A 3 B 4 C

7
Add -s: games
Add -es: watches
Remove -f, add -ves: wives, scarves
Remove -y, add -ies: cities, diaries
Irregular: children, men

8
1 Can you sing? Yes, I/we can.
2 Can your husband cook? No, he can't.
3 Can she speak Spanish and Portuguese? Yes, she can.
4 Can you do judo? Yes, I/we can.
5 Can a DVD player send emails? No, it can't.

9a

	job	family	verb	adjective
1 daughters	☐	✓	☐	☐
2 leave	☐	☐	✓	☐
3 invent	☐	☐	✓	☐
4 get up	☐	☐	✓	☐
5 chef	✓	☐	☐	☐
6 play	☐	☐	✓	☐
7 horrible	☐	☐	☐	✓
8 uncle	☐	✓	☐	☐
9 pretty	☐	☐	☐	✓

9b
1 doctor 2 uncle 3 daughters 4 pretty 5 leave 6 get up 7 invent
8 play 9 horrible

10
2 j 3 d 4 i 5 h 6 e 7 b 8 a 9 g 10 f

Unit 4

Lesson 4.1

1a
2

1b
1 tomatoes and cheese 2 What is 3 a special pizza 4 restaurants
5 more than 100,000 (pizza restaurants) 6 original pizza 7 Naples, Italy

2a/2b
Countable: tomatoes, banana, beans, burger, hot dog, potato
Uncountable: cheese, beef, chicken, seafood, pineapple, bread, rice,
tea, water

3
1 isn't 2 much 3 many 4 are 5 is 6 a lot of 7 much 8 is 9 a lot of
10 many

4a
1 beans 2 salad 3 dried fruit 4 tomato 5 orange juice 6 eggs
7 sandwich 8 hot dog

4b
B salad C hot dog D sandwich E tomato F orange juice

5
2 e 3 d 4 c 5 f 6 a

6
1 How much rice do you buy at the supermarket?
2 How much water do you drink every day?
3 How much oranges do you buy at the market?
4 How many bananas does your family eat every week?
5 How much coffee do you drink at the weekend?
6 How many burgers do you eat every week?
(Students' own answers.)

7a
1 T 2 F 3 T 4 T 5 F

7b
1 A 2 A 3 K 4 K 5 A 6 K 7 K

Lesson 4.2

1a
2

1b
1 2 2 4 3 1 4 6 and 7 5 3 6 2

2
B jar C carton D bottle E packet F can G tube H box

3a
1 bottle 2 box 3 carton 4 tube 5 packet 6 bag 7 jar

3b
1 jar 2 bottle 3 box 4 can 5 carton 6 tube 7 packet

4
(in any order)
2 some nuts 3 some dried fruit 4 a can of tomatoes
5 a potato 6 some lamb 7 some salt

5
1 any mineral water 2 some lamb 3 some dried fruit 4 any potatoes
5 some chocolate 6 any money 7 any cash 8 a credit card
9 a biscuit 10 any biscuits

6a

/æ/	/ʌ/
carrot	hungry
grandparents	money
laptop	nightclub
package	sunbathe
programme	Sunday
	unemployed

7
2 e 3 f 4 a 5 d 6 b

Lesson 4.3

1a
1 Yes, she does. 2 Yes, she does. 3 She pays by credit card.

1b
1 €8.50 2 small tomato salad 3 €2.45 4 small cup of coffee
5 €12.95

1c
1 €8.95 2 €3.00 3 €2.00 4 €2.75

2a
1 How much is a large seafood and pineapple pizza?
2 How much is a large tomato salad/small seafood salad?
3 How much is a small beef and tomato pizza?

2b
2 c 3 d 4 b 5 a 6 e

3
1 much 2 Do 3 want 4 drink 5 I'll 6 is 7 by

4a
1 her 2 him 3 them 4 us

4b
1 them, No, they're for me. 2 him, No, they're for us.
3 you, No, it's for her. 4 her, No, it's for him. 5 them, No, it's for her.

5
1 He loves her. 2 We don't like it. 3 They help us with it.
4 They visit them every Saturday afternoon.
5 We play football with him. 6 She uses it every day.
7 Do you want to have lunch with us?
8 Does he want to take a photo with it?
9 Can we stay with you?
10 Does he know how to use it?

Unit 5

Lesson 5.1

1a
2

1b
1, B

1c
1 T 2 F 3 F 4 F 5 T

2a
Rooms: living room, dining room, kitchen, bedroom, shower room
Other parts/features: windows, air conditioning, garden, patio

2b

Types of home: apartment, detached house, terraced house, villa
Rooms: attic, bathroom, bedroom, cellar, dining room, kitchen, shower room, study
Other parts/features: air conditioning, central heating, double glazing, garage, garden, patio, solar panels, terrace

3

1 There are 2 Are there 3 There's 4 There isn't 5 Is there
6 There isn't 7 There aren't 8 There's 9 Is there 10 Are there

4

1 there's 2 There's 3 there's 4 there aren't 5 bedrooms 6 bathroom
7 There's 8 kitchen 9 there isn't 10 There's 11 there isn't

5

Students' own answers.

6

1 under 2 on 3 between 4 in 5 behind/in front of/next to 6 on
7 next to 8 near

Lesson 5.2

1a

2 f 3 d 4 a 5 c 6 e
2 music system 3 microwave 4 cupboard 5 dishwasher
6 dining table

1b

2 washing machine 3 dining table 4 microwave 5 dishwasher
6 music system

2

1 coffee table 2 sofa 3 TV 4 fridge 5 desk 6 bed 7 chair 8 lamp

3

1 I've got two brothers. 2 They've got a swimming pool.
3 Álvaro's got a laptop computer. 4 We've got a new sofa.
5 You've got a phone message. 6 I've got three children.

4

1 We haven't got a big kitchen. 2 Has your girlfriend got a good job?
3 She hasn't got a mobile phone. 4 Have they got a microwave?
5 He hasn't got a credit card.

5

1 Has your town got a shopping centre? Yes, it has./No, it hasn't.
2 Has your town got an airport? Yes, it has./No, it hasn't.
3 Have you got any children? Yes, I have./No, I haven't.
4 Have you got any brothers or sisters? Yes, I have./No, I haven't.

6

Students' own answers.

7a

B

7b

1 've/have got two 2 's/has got three 3 's/has got three
4 've/have got forty

7c

1 Yes, they have. 2 No, she hasn't. 3 Yes, he has. 4 Yes, it has.
5 No, they haven't. 6 Yes, they have.

8

	/æ/	/ɒ/
1 hospital		✓
2 pocket		✓
3 tap	✓	
4 shop		✓
5 packet	✓	
6 hot		✓

Lesson 5.3

1a

1 (across) COLD 1 (down) CITY 2 LAKE 3 (across) BEAUTIFUL
3 (down) BEACH 4 FOREST 5 GREEN 6 HUGE 7 ISLAND 8 DRY
9 BUSY   'Cold' is not in the clues.

1b

1 wet 2 friendly 3 dry 4 high 5 low 6 busy 7 green 8 hot 9 high
10 green

2a

1 coun/try/side 2 com/plete 3 de/cide 4 fam/ous 5 moun/tain
6 o/pin/ion 7 trop/ic/al 8 vill/age

2c

Words with two syllables, stress on 1st syllable: famous, mountain, village
Words with two syllables, stress on 2nd syllable: complete, decide
Words with three syllables, stress on 1st syllable: countryside, tropical
Words with three syllables, stress on 2nd syllable: opinion

3

Students' own answers.

4

2 The police officer's job is very interesting.
3 The Empire State is really tall. 4 The car isn't very big.
5 Brad Pitt is very famous. 6 Chicken and potatoes is quite healthy.

5a

1 It's in the south-east of Scotland.
2 It's got a lot of museums, theatres and restaurants.
3 There's an arts festival in Edinburgh every summer.
4 Glasgow is near Edinburgh.
5 There are lakes and mountains near the city.
6 Yes, he does, because it's very friendly and beautiful.

5b

How to say where you come from/live: I live in …
How to say what kind of place it is and where it's near: It's a really (interesting) place … , It's quite near …
How to describe the landscape: There are (some lakes and mountains north of the two cities) …
How to give your opinion: I (really) like … because

Unit 6

Lesson 6.1

1

1 There was a zoo in Lake Road.
2 There were shops in Lake Road.
3 There was a factory in Station Road.
4 There was a station in Station Road.
5 There was a cinema in Harley Street.
6 There was a hospital in Harley Street.
7 There were houses in the park.

2

1 Was there a factory in Station Road? Yes, there was.
2 What was there in Green Street? There were shops and houses.
3 Was there a nightclub in Harley Street? No, there wasn't. There was a cinema.
4 Were there apartments in Station Road? No, there weren't. There was a factory and a station.
5 What was there next to the cinema? There was a hospital (next to the cinema).
6 What was there in the park? There were houses.

3

4, 7, 1, 8, 2, 6, 3, 5

4a

stayed, wanted, phoned, walked, visited, called, wanted, tried

4b

1 walked 2 stayed 3 decided 4 visited 5 wanted 6 phoned/called
7 tried

5

1 performed at the concert hall
2 She opened a/the new supermarket
3 She watched the DVD of a/the concert with Mike
4 She planned her trip to New York
5 She played football with the boys

6a

1 walked 2 worked 3 played 4 cooked 5 helped 6 watched 7 relaxed

6b

1 walked 2 7:00 3 waited 4 the bus 5 worked 6 4:00
7 repaired cars all day 8 cooked dinner for his family
9 studied from 7:30 to 9:30 10 listened to music

7a

/t/ worked, cooked
/d/ repaired, listened
/ɪd/ started, waited

Lesson 6.2

1a
2

1b

Suggested answers:
went away for the weekend, we had three days there, lovely old
buildings, visited museums and an art gallery, stayed in a good hotel,
we loved the city

2

1 F: They were away for three days.
2 F: They went to the Picasso Museum.
3 F: They went to a restaurant with friends for dinner on Saturday
   evening.
4 T
5 F: The weather was good on Sunday, but it rained on Saturday.

3

1 fly 2 leave/rain 3 arrive 4 stay 5 go/love 6 visit/see 7 walk
8 visit/meet 9 eat 10 buy 11 spend/take 12 have

4a

Regular: loved, rained, stayed, visited, walked
Irregular: bought, ate, flew, went, had, left, met, saw, spent, took

4b

1 We flew from Bristol airport on Friday.
2 We had a great time.
3 We stayed in a cheap hotel in the city centre.
4 On Saturday we went sightseeing.
5 We visited a lot of museums and galleries.
6 We walked round the city in the afternoon.
7 We ate at a lovely fish restaurant in the evening.
8 We bought some clothes and shoes.
9 We spent a lot of money.
10 Last month we had a city break in Istanbul.

5

H	O	S	P	I	T	A	L				P	
			P			A					A	
			A				B	A	R		R		F
M			R				A		K		K		A
U			T				N						C
S	U	P	E	R	M	A	R	K	E	T			T
E			M										O
U			E										R
M			N		A	R	T	G	A	L	L	E	R	Y
			I									
	M	A	R	K	E	T						
			P									
	C	L	O	T	H	E	S	S	H	O	P	
			R									
		S	T	A	T	I	O	N				

Lesson 6.3

1a
2/two years

1b

4, 6, 1, 7, 5, 2, 3

1c

1 There were thirty-three people on the journey: Lewis and Clark,
   thirty men and an Indian woman, Sacagawea.
2 The Dakota Indians helped them find the Pacific Ocean.
3 They measured everything for their maps.
4 They discovered that North America was a huge place.

2

1 Where did Lewis and Clark start 2 When did they start
3 Was the weather 4 Where did they stay/Who did they stay with
5 Where did they travel 6 When did they find 7 When did they finish
8 What did they discover

3

1 Did, No, they didn't. 2 help, Yes, they did. 3 Did, No, they didn't.
4 travel, Yes, they did.

4

1 William Shakespeare didn't write Don Quixote.
2 My great-grandparents didn't own a car.
3 Queen Elizabeth I wasn't married.
4 People didn't have mobile phones in the 1970s.
5 My father didn't go to university.
6 In the eighteenth century people didn't wear jeans.
7 I didn't do my homework yesterday.

5

1 in the 16th century 2 in the 1990s 3 yesterday 4 ago
5 last Saturday afternoon 6 last night

6a

1 No, I like potatoes. 2 No, I'm Canadian. 3 No, she's thirsty.
4 No, we arrived on Thursday.

7

1 Did, speak 2 Did, want, did 3 Why, decided, job 4 When, married

Review and consolidation 4–6

1

Countable nouns: coin, dishwasher, lamp, receipt
Uncountable nouns: bread, butter, money, rice, sugar

2

1 much 2 any 3 a lot of, some 4 many 5 much 6 a 7 many 8 a
9 some

3

1 him 2 them 3 it 4 you 5 her 6 me 7 us 8 them 9 her

4

1 there's 2 Is there 3 there is 4 there are 5 Is there 6 there isn't
7 Are there 8 there aren't 9 there isn't

5

2 The new sports centre is very modern. 3 This film is really boring.
4 My diet is really unhealthy. 5 This beach isn't very popular.

6

1 Have you got a microwave? No, I haven't.
2 Has Sarah got a credit card? Yes, she has.
3 Have your parents got a big garden? No, they haven't.
4 Have we got any biscuits? Yes, we have.
5 Has the dog got any food? Yes, it/he/she has.

7a

1 decided 2 ate 3 went 4 left 5 met 6 produced 7 started 8 stayed
9 stopped 10 wanted 11 worked

7b

1 didn't want 2 worked 3 stopped 4 decided 5 went 6 stayed 7 met
8 started 9 ate 10 produced 11 Did, have

7c

1 He didn't want to study at university. He wanted money/to (go to)
   work.
2 He didn't stay at the factory for ten years. He stayed/worked there
   for five years.
3 He didn't marry a woman in Africa. He married a woman in India.
4 They didn't open an Indian factory. They opened an Indian restaurant.
5 They didn't produce Indian food for schools. They produced Indian
   food (in cans) for supermarkets.

8a

Food and drink: cola, lamb, potato, seafood
Rooms: bathroom, cellar, dining room, kitchen, study
Furniture/equipment: bed, cupboard, fridge, microwave, table
Places in a town: bank, chemist's, newsagent's, post office, station

8b

1 station 2 seafood 3 bathroom 4 microwave 5 lamb 6 newsagent's
7 cupboard 8 bank

Unit 7

Lesson 7.1

1
2

2
b 1 f 2 d 3 a 4 c 5 e 6

3a

	Words before	Words after	Noun, verb or adjective
thief	the	broke into	noun
broke into	the thief	(the) car	verb
cell	put him in a	in the police station	noun
fake	(the) business made the	1,000-euro notes	adjective

3b

1 broke into 2 thief 3 steal 4 cell

4

1 Inside a car. 2 No, he didn't.
3 He tried to steal the note./He broke into the car and took the note.
4 Because people in the street called them. 5 To the police station.
6 In a cell. 7 One night. 8 A local business.
9 To advertise a competition. 10 1,000 euros.

5a

1 set off 2 gave back 3 pull out 4 handed in 5 put together 6 pick up

5b

break into/broke into

6

1 b 2 a

7

1 a 2 The 3 the 4 a 5 the 6 the 7 a 8 the 9 the 10 the

8

1 a 2 a 3 the 4 the 5 the 6 the 7 an 8 a 9 The 10 a

Lesson 7.2

1a
likes, difficult

1b

1 At the university 2 Chicago 3 10/ten 4 Jeremy

1c

1 Amanda 2 Stefan 3 Dieter 4 Henry 5 Elizabeth 6 Jeremy 7 Clara

2a

A Jeremy B Stefan C Clara E Dieter F Amanda G Surinda H Henry
I Melanie J Alvaro

2b

1 Two 2 Two 3 Two 4 Four

3

1 old 2 unattractive 3 friendly 4 horrible 5 fair 6 confident
7 handsome 8 bald

4

Students' own answers.

5

2 a 3 e 4 h 5 c 6 b 7 d 8 f

6

2 CDs 3 salad 4 sports centre 5 swimming pool

7

1 I like hot places, but Sally likes cold ones.
2 Can I have six large salads and two small ones, please?
3 Do you want the British spelling or the American one?
4 We've got three bedrooms. I sleep in the big one.
5 Do you want the blue chairs, the red ones or the yellow ones?
6 I'd like four tuna sandwiches and a chicken one, please.
7 Don't wear the red shoes. Wear the black ones.

Lesson 7.3

1a
2

1b

1 F 2 T 3 T 4 F 5 F 6 T

2

1 18th November 2 August 3 2nd January 4 22nd July 5 24th August
6 November 7 April 8 four

3

1 the fourteenth of July 2 the twenty-third of April
3 the seventeenth of March 4 the twenty-sixth of December
5 the twenty-second of April 6 the nineteenth of October
7 the first of September 8 the fifteenth of January

4

2 D 3 E 4 A 5 B

5

1 your 2 their 3 ours 4 yours 5 hers 6 our 7 my 8 her

6

1 belongs to you 2 is mine 3 is theirs 4 is ours
5 doesn't belong to them 6 isn't yours 7 are ours

7

1 ours 2 mine 3 hers 4 his 5 yours

8a
1 third 2 something

8b
1 3 2 2 3 3 4 2

Unit 8

Lesson 8.1

1
1 D 2 E 3 I 4 G 5 F 6 H 7 A 8 C

2a
Because she's feeling sick.

2b
1 B 2 C 3 A 4 D 5 E 6 H 7 G 8 F

3a

1 Martina 2 Tanika 3 Annette 4 Justine 5 Charlie 6 Darren 7 Tanika
8 Clare and Hannah 9 George and Andy 10 Annette 11 Justine
12 Martina

3b

1 Charlie is listening to the singer. He's eating a burger.
2 Annette is talking to Charlie. She's eating some crisps.
3 Clare and Hannah are sitting on the grass. They're drinking cola.
4 Darren is playing football. He isn't listening to Tanika/the singer.
5 George and Andy aren't talking/are talking. They're trying different food.
6 Justine is taking photos. She's watching some/the dancers.
7 Tanika is singing (some (pop) songs). She's playing the guitar.

4

1 Is Tanika playing the piano? No, she isn't. She's playing the guitar.
2 Are Charlie and Annette watching (the) dancers? No, they aren't. They're listening to a/the singer/Tanika.
3 Is Justine making a video? No, she isn't. She's taking photos.
4 Are George and Andy sitting down? No, they aren't. They're walking around (the food stalls).
5 Are Zamboyo singing? No, they aren't. They're dancing.
6 Is Clare talking to Darren? No, she isn't. She's talking to Hannah.
7 Is Darren playing tennis? No, he isn't. He's playing football.
8 Are Clare and Hannah eating crisps? No, they aren't. They're drinking cola.

5

1 I'm <u>having</u> a good <u>time</u>. 2 She's <u>playing</u> the gu<u>itar</u>.
3 He's <u>eating</u> a <u>burger</u>. 4 He <u>isn't</u> <u>listen</u>ing.
5 They're <u>sitting</u> on the <u>grass</u>. 6 They <u>aren't</u> talking.
7 We're <u>watching</u> some <u>dan</u>cers.

6

1 talking 2 the left 3 listening 4 of the picture 5 at the back 6 there are

Lesson 8.2

1a
wool

1b
1 black and grey 2 wool 3 a loose skirt 4 It's very warm.
5 long and loose

2a
1 wool 2 loose 3 leather 4 evening 5 silk 6 gold 7 shoes

3a
1 cotton 2 formal 3 jacket 4 jeans 5 leather 6 light 7 loose
8 pullover 9 shirt 10 skirt 11 smart 12 suit 13 thick 14 tight 15 wool

3b
Clothes: jacket, jeans, shirt, skirt, suit
Adjectives: formal, light, loose, smart, thick, tight
Materials: cotton, leather, silk, wool

4
2 a tight shirt 3 a formal suit 4 a light skirt 5 loose jeans
6 a thick coat

5
Suggested answers:
Summer: jeans, sandals, shorts, T-shirt
Winter: coat, gloves, pullover, scarf
Formal: suit
Informal: jeans, shorts, T-shirt

6
1 We bought a comfortable leather sofa.
2 In warm weather I prefer casual cotton clothes.
3 Do you have a smart black suit?
4 Uncle Derek drives an expensive German car.
5 Kirsty wore a beautiful silk wedding dress.
6 Darren's wearing a scruffy wool pullover today.
7 My brother's got a lovely Japanese girlfriend.
8 Why are there so many boring old films on TV these days?

7
1 <u>black fashionable</u> fashionable black
2 <u>expensive looks</u> looks expensive
3 <u>cotton nice</u> nice cotton
4 <u>very polite were</u> were very polite
5 <u>Italian smart</u> smart Italian
6 <u>nice looks</u> looks nice

Lesson 8.3

1a
1 cold + ld = cold 2 fog + gy = foggy 3 rain + ing = raining
4 sno + wing = snowing 5 su + nny = sunny 6 wa + rm = warm
7 win + dy = windy

1b
1 cloudy 2 sunny, warm 3 cold, snowing 4 foggy 5 raining

2a
1 2, 1, 1, 1, 2   2 1, 1, 2, 1   3 2, 2, 1, 1   4 1, 1, 2, 1, 2

3a
the sun: good and bad
hot weather: bad for us
cold weather: good and bad

3b
1 F 2 T 3 T 4 F

4
1 important 2 suntan 3 depression 4 sick 5 dark

5a
1 She's waiting to go on the sunbed.
2 She usually spends ten minutes on the sunbed.
3 She is meeting her fitness instructor.
4 She uses the gym three or four times a week.

5b
Actions happening now: 2, 3, 6
Actions that happen regularly: 5, 7, 8

6
2 he sells men's clothes. 3 he plays computer games.
4 he eats a burger with (his) friends. 6 He's swimming in the sea.
7 He's eating fish at a restaurant. 8 He's playing football on the beach.

Unit 9

Lesson 9.1

1a
e-books and real books

1b
1 real book 2 real book 3 e-book reader 4 real book 5 real book

2
2 an e-book reader 3 after the late 1990s 4 thousands
5 You can change it. 6 It can break.

3
1 <u>use</u> go 2 <u>read</u> listen to 3 <u>use</u> watch 4 <u>watch</u> read 5 <u>listen to</u> use

4
1 Real books are more attractive than e-books.
2 E-book readers are lighter than several real books.
3 Coats are warmer than jackets.
4 Chicago is windier than New York.
5 Japanese is more difficult than English.
6 Santiago is smaller than Mexico City.

5a
1 cold – hot 2 difficult – easy 3 loose – tight 4 quiet – noisy
5 smart – casual 6 ugly – handsome 7 unhealthy – healthy
8 untidy – tidy

5b
2 Ken is more handsome than Mike./Mike is uglier than Ken.
3 The living room is tidier than the bedroom./The bedroom is untidier than the living room.
4 Emma is noisier than Caroline./Caroline is quieter than Emma.
5 Harriet is smarter than Harry./Harry is more casual than Harriet.
6 Egypt is hotter than Greenland./Greenland is colder than Egypt.

6
1 younger than 2 nicer than 3 more exciting than 4 colder than
5 prettier than

7a
1 young<u>er</u> <u>than</u> 2 nic<u>er</u> <u>than</u> 3 more exciting <u>than</u> 4 cold<u>er</u> <u>than</u>
5 prett<u>ier</u> <u>than</u>

8
1 find 2 think/believe 3 In 4 don't 5 think

Lesson 9.2

1a

S	Y	D	X	X	F	Y	A	O	A	S	M	Y	C
R	N	O	H	N	F	U	T	T	D	N	U	R	A
Q	P	C	T	O	O	F	J	Z	V	N	S	Y	R
B	T	U	O	H	R	D	V	I	E	Q	I	H	T
G	H	M	Y	M	R	R	U	N	W	C	S	O
U	R	E	Q	A	E	B	O	T	T	S	A	R	O
B	I	N	O	F	D	D	V	R	U	G	L	M	N
F	L	T	O	L	T	Z	Y	O	R	P	A	A	S
I	L	A	I	S	S	E	C	Q	E	R	Y	E	G
L	E	R	L	O	V	E	S	T	O	R	Y	G	Y
N	R	Y	J	T	T	O	A	J	R	X	C	B	W
S	C	I	E	N	C	E	F	I	C	T	I	O	N

1b

1 comedy 2 horror 3 cartoon 4 adventure 5 musical 6 science fiction
7 thriller 8 documentary

2

1 the most best the best 2 the bigger the biggest
3 newest the newest 4 the most cheap the cheapest
5 the most attractivest the most attractive

3

1 Jane is the tallest (girl). 2 Yvonne's child is the youngest (baby).
3 Luis is the cleverest (student). 4 Antonio is the heaviest (man).
5 Peter is the most romantic (boyfriend).

4a

1 The oldest tree is in Sweden.
2 The loudest rock band is Green Day.
3 The biggest passenger plane is the Airbus 380.
4 The driest desert is the Atacama Desert in Chile.
5 The fastest animal is the cheetah.
6 The most dangerous roads are in India.
7 The highest mountain is Mount Everest.
8 The most poisonous animal is a frog.

4b

Students' own answers.

5a

1 3   2 2   3 1   4 1, 3   5 1

6

1 drama 2 accident 3 businessman 4 strong

7

1 He thinks *It's a wonderful (after)life* is the funniest film.
2 He thinks *The Ghost* is the most interesting.
3 He thinks *The Joneses* is the most unusual.
4 *The Ghost* is the longest film of the three.
5 *The Joneses* is the shortest.

8

	Film	Type	Time	Dan's rating (✳)
1		*thriller*	127 minutes	✳✳✳✳
2		comedy horror	100 minutes	✳✳
3		comedy drama	96 minutes	✳✳✳

Lesson 9.3

1a

2 e 3 b 4 d 5 a

1b

1 German 2 Monday 3 From the website 4 At the Sage-Club
5 Beethoven and Mozart

2

1 b 2 c 3 c 4 b 5 c 6 b 7 b 8 b

3

1 love 2 prefer 3 listening 4 don't like 5 than 6 staying 7 listen
8 to 9 swimming 10 stay

4a

1 a 2 a 3 b

4b

1 love loves 2 liking like 3 eat eating 4 of than 5 hating hate 6 of to
7 the walking walking 8 watch watching

5

1 Dario prefers traditional art to modern art.
2 The children prefer playing to reading.
3 I prefer adventure films to horror films.
4 Clara prefers watching television to listening to music.
5 We prefer going to concerts to visiting museums.
6 I prefer French food to Italian food.

6

1 A: Is she his new girlfriend? B: No, she isn't.

2 A: I bought a new phone. B: Was it expensive?

3 A: Are you married? B: Yes, I am.

4 A: I don't like poems. B: Do you like novels?

5 A: Is he handsome? B: Yes, he is.

Review and consolidation 7–9

1

1 the 2 The 3 the 4 the 5 a 6 the 7 the 8 a 9 a 10 the

2

1 our house ours 2 my wallet mine 3 the pink flowers the pink ones
4 The bus The one 5 their house theirs 6 your bag yours

3

1 Dan and Gemma are making a Chinese meal.
2 What's Steve doing in the garden?
3 Laura is wearing a long skirt this evening.
4 What are you watching on TV?
5 Mum isn't speaking to Dad at the moment.
6 The boys are playing tennis in the park.
7 Our daughter is sleeping in her room.
8 Where are you planning to go on holiday?
9 I'm not having a very good time.
10 What are you carrying in that bag?

4

1 usually work 2 don't get 3 'm having 4 'm waiting 5 's coming
6 is bringing 7 like 8 cook 9 are you doing

5

2 an old Italian painting 3 a scruffy wool pullover
4 an expensive German car 5 a friendly Chinese student
6 a comfortable leather sofa 7 a famous American statue
8 a tight white T-shirt

6

1 Mac is heavier than Ian. 2 Mac is older than Joe. 3 Mac is the tallest.
4 Joe is shorter than Mac. 5 Ian is the youngest.
6 Joe is heavier than Ian. 7 Joe is the shortest.
8 Ian is younger than Mac. 9 Joe is older than Ian.
10 Joe is the heaviest.

7

1 than to 2 go going 3 to eating eating 4 play playing
5 to doing doing 6 swim swimming

8a

1 ballet 2 tight 3 pullover 4 slim 5 comedy 6 hot 7 sandals

8b

1 hot 2 slim 3 ballet 4 pullover 5 comedy 6 tight 7 sandals

Unit 10

Lesson 10.1

1a
3

1b
1 petrol station 2 top speed 3 wheels 4 energy 5 scooter 6 connect

1c
Suggested answers:
Advantages: Riding it is easy. You don't need a lot of energy.
It's easy to park. You don't need to go to the petrol station.
You don't need a driving licence.
Disadvantages: It isn't very fast. It's quite heavy.

2a
2 C 3 A 4 F 5 B 6 E

2b
1 a helicopter 2 a bicycle 3 a water bus 4 a taxi 5 an electric tram

3
1 garage 2 boat 3 suburb 4 bicycle

4
1 Watching horror films is scary.
2 Eating lots of fruit and vegetables is healthy.
3 Driving in fog is dangerous.
4 Learning a foreign language is difficult.
5 Swimming in warm water is relaxing.

5
1 Parking a car in big cities is difficult.
2 Getting information from the Internet is easy.
3 Sending flowers to your wife is romantic.
4 Getting an email from your best friend is nice.
5 Watching the news on TV is interesting.

6
1 to 2 One-way 3 Standard 4 is 5 direct 6 stops 7 at

Lesson 10.2

1a
holiday rep

1b and 1c
2 ✓ 3 ✓ last winter 4 ✗ 5 ✓ 6 ✗ 7 ✓ last summer
8 ✓ when she was at university

2
Della's answers:
2 No, I haven't. 3 Yes, I've been to San Antonio, in Ibiza.
Students' own answers.

3a
1 went 2 Have 3 've 4 haven't 5 been 6 've 7 went 8 been
9 haven't

4
2 f 3 b 4 c 5 g 6 a 7 e

5
1 I've been bungee jumping.
2 We haven't been to Bangkok.
3 Have you been to London?
4 Have they been on a package holiday?
5 John and Julie haven't been to Australia.
6 I haven't been on an adventure holiday.
7 Our parents have been to Florida.
8 Have you been to an IMAX cinema?
9 We've been hiking in the mountains.
10 Have your cousins been to Disneyland?

6
2 Have you been to New York?
3 Have you been to a concert?
4 Have you been to a football match?
5 Have you been to Paris?/Have you visited the Eiffel Tower?
6 Have you been to an Internet café?
Student's own answers.

7a

	/ɪ/	/ə/
1 I haven't been to Rimini.	✓	
2 Have you been to Australia?	✓	
3 We've been bungee jumping.	✓	
4 Have you been on a horse?		✓
5 Have you been to Italy?	✓	
6 Have you been to Madrid?		✓

Lesson 10.3

1a
3

1b
1 a 2 c 3 f 4 b 5 e 6 d

2
1 T 2 F 3 F 4 F 5 F 6 T 7 T 8 F

3a
1 ✓ 2 ✓ 3 ✓ 4 ✗ 5 ✓ 6 ✓ 7 ✗

3b
1 Has Mae been into space? Yes, she has.
2 Has she danced on stage? Yes, she has.
3 Has she appeared on TV? Yes, she has.
4 Has she sailed around the world? No, she hasn't.
5 Has she travelled to Africa? Yes, she has.
6 Has she produced music and dance shows? Yes, she has.
7 Has she worked in Australia? No, she hasn't.

4a
1 flown 2 ridden 3 eaten 4 met 5 seen

4b
1 have flown 2 have, seen 3 Have, met 4 have, eaten 5 has driven

5
1 Sue has run a marathon, but she hasn't cycled 50 kilometres.
2 Lyle hasn't climbed a mountain, but he has run a marathon.
3 Maria hasn't run a marathon, but she has cycled 50 kilometres.
4 Jack hasn't climbed a mountain, but he has cycled 50 kilometres.
5 Leila has climbed a mountain, but she hasn't cycled 50 kilometres.

6
1 climb Mount Everest 2 fly a small aircraft 3 row a small boat
4 crossed the Sahara Desert

7a
1 b 2 a 3 b 4 a 5 b

Unit 11

Lesson 11.1

1a
2

1b
2 electronic devices 3 documents 4 luggage

1c
2 c 3 f 4 a 5 b 6 d

2
1 necessary 2 necessary 3 possible 4 not possible 5 not possible
6 necessary 7 not necessary 8 necessary 9 not possible

3
1 You can't take drinks onto the plane.
2 You can't take food onto the plane.
3 You have to be at check-in two hours before your departure time.
4 You have to turn off your mobile phone before you board the plane.
5 You have to wear your seat belt during the flight.

4
1 can't drive a car when you are only fifteen years old
2 can bring a friend to the party (if I want to)
3 can't use our mobile phones in my office
4 have to show your receipt to the manager
5 can't park near the theatre
6 doesn't have to pay because she's a member of the club
7 can pay in cash or by credit card
8 don't have to get visas to go to Canada

5
1 can't 2 can 3 have to 4 can't 5 have to 6 have to 7 can 8 have to

6a
/f/   /v/
You don't ha<u>v</u>e to ha<u>v</u>e a French visa.

6b

	/f/	/v/
1 Do you ha<u>v</u>e a car?	☐	✓
2 I'<u>v</u>e got a question.	☐	✓
3 Let's ha<u>v</u>e a drink tomorrow.	☐	✓
4 Do you ha<u>v</u>e to leave now?	✓	☐

Lesson 11.2

1
1 c 2 a 3 b

2a
1 P 2 P 3 A 4 N

2b

	Polly	Alana	Neil
1	4		4
2	Glasgow	*Texas*	London
3	12 yrs		*14 yrs*
4	French (at school)	no	Spanish (at university)
5	English	physics, chemistry	history, art
6	no	yes	yes

3a
Underline: university, secondary school, technical college, elementary school, teacher training college
Circle: biology, French, hairdressing, Spanish, history, art, physics, chemistry, English

3b
1 French, Spanish, English
2 university, technical college, teacher training college
3 biology, physics, chemistry 4 elementary school

4
1 When, start 2 Where did 3 What do 4 What, favourite

5a
1 How many 2 Who 3 Where 4 What 5 How 6 When

5b
2 What do you do at the weekend?/Where do you go in the evenings?
3 When did you start learning English?
4 Who do you live with?
5 How do you get to the school?
6 What did you watch on TV yesterday?
7 Which subjects did you do?/How many subjects have you got on Monday?

5c
Students' own answers.

6a
1 When did you start school?
2 Where did you go to university?
3 What do you teach?
4 What was your favourite subject?

7
1 download 2 podcasts 3 forum 4 posts

Lesson 11.3

1
Adjectives: full-time, part-time, professional, well-qualified
Types of education: distance learning courses, evening classes
People learning: student, trainee
People teaching: lecturer, trainer, tutor

2
1 a professional 2 part-time 3 students 4 a distance learning course
5 lecturer

3a
3

3b
1 Wednesday morning, Wednesday afternoon, Thursday morning and Thursday afternoon
2 No, he can't. 3 Bryony Addams

4a
1 Tariq Raschid 2 AX327 3 Thursday morning 4 Wednesday

4b
3

5
1 Leave your shoes outside the door.
2 Write your name at the top of every page.
3 Don't drive faster than 50 kph on this road.
4 Complete the form with a black pen.

6
2 Don't park here. 3 Don't put it in the washing machine.
4 Please take your rubbish home. 5 Don't talk in the library.
6 Don't play ball on the grass.

Unit 12

Lesson 12.1

1a
1 near the sea/coast 2 on a beach 3 tomorrow

1b
1 white-water rafting 2 canyon 3 island 4 sailing 5 trekking

2a
The photo shows Anthony and Belinda. The map shows where Anthony is going this summer.

2b
1 f 2 e 3 g 4 a 5 d 6 b 7 c

2c
1 trekking 2 drive 3 isn't 4 ten days

3a
1 Are, going to 2 'm going to 3 're going to 4 're going to
5 're going to 6 'm going to 7 Is, going to 8 's going to
9 're going to 10 're going to

4
1 I'm going to finish the course in September.
2 No, I'm going to send an email tomorrow.
3 This year they are going to stay with friends in Spain.
4 Henry is going to go sailing in Canada next year.
5 She isn't going to study science at university.
6 But I'm going to study this weekend.

5
Suggested answers:
2 I'm going to lose weight/get fit.
3 We're going to get married.
4 I'm going to get a job/be a computer programmer.
5 We're going to buy a new TV.

6
1 He's going to fly to <u>Rome</u>. 2 We're going to buy a <u>car</u>.
3 I'm going to see the <u>doctor</u>. 4 She's going to meet my <u>parents</u>.
5 They're going to stay at <u>home</u>. 6 He's going to be a <u>painter</u>.

7

1 later this year 2 the week after next 3 In three years' time
4 next year 5 four years from now 6 the day after tomorrow
7 in two weeks' time

Lesson 12.2

1a

a 2 b 3 c 1

1b

1 Twitter 2 Directed a film
3 An American woman (who wanted to marry the king of England in
the 1930s). 4 £56 million 5 their cleaner.

1c

1 Girl 2 London, musical 3 million, are, cleaner

2

1 nice 2 shows 3 name 4 cold 5 blue 6 clever 7 mine 8 free 9 alone

3

1 do 2 hold 3 name 4 mine

4

2 c 3 a 4 f 5 b 6 e
2 You can use a computer to send emails.
3 She's joining a gym to get fit.
4 Mike uses his bicycle to commute to work.
5 We went to Warsaw to visit our grandparents.
6 I'm going to improve my English to get a better job.

5

1 Jane flew to Berlin to visit her boyfriend.
2 My son uses his computer to play games.
3 I'm going to get an MP3 player to listen to music.
4 We always go to the market to buy fresh food.
5 My brother went to St. Petersburg to see the Hermitage Museum.

6a

1 talk to talk 2 buying buy

Lesson 12.3

1a

go around the world, work for a charity, win a lot of money,
be a rock singer

1b

1 fly around the world and see lots of interesting places
2 work for a charity 3 be a rock singer

2

1 doing nothing 2 to travel, flying 3 to work for
4 wouldn't like (to do), to be, playing, singing

3a

1 I wouldn't like working 2 I really love to do
3 I would like to becoming 4 most of them like learn
5 I really don't like to take 6 I really like starting

3b

1 I wouldn't like to work 2 I really love doing 3 I would like to become
4 most of them like learning 5 I really don't like taking
6 I'd really like to start

4

2 He would like to be a racing driver because he likes driving fast.
3 She would like to get/buy a good music system because she likes
listening to music.
4 He would like to be a teacher because he likes helping young
people.
5 She would like to be a holiday rep because she likes visiting
different countries.
6 She would like to have lots of grandchildren because she likes
being with children.

5

Students' own answers.

6

/aɪ/: mine, size, light, height, white, try
/eɪ/: hate, late, wait, main, say, train

Review and consolidation 10–12

1

1 ✗ fly – flying 2 ✗ are – is 3 ✓ 4 ✗ pay – paying 5 ✗ are – is 6 ✓

2

1 haven't 2 Has, has 3 Have, haven't 4 Has, 's 5 Have, 've

3

1 I haven't driven a sports car. 2 Have you taken the driving test?
3 Has she been to New York? 4 I haven't seen that film.
5 We haven't visited Australia. 6 Have you flown in a helicopter?
7 Has Lena climbed a mountain? 8 We haven't been horse riding.

4a

a Don't bring b Show c Don't use d Bring

4b

2 You can smoke in the garden.
3 You can't bring food or drinks into the classrooms.
4 You can get coffee and tea in the college café.
5 You have to show an identity card when they come into the college.
6 You can't use mobile phones during lessons.
7 You can use the computers in the library in the evenings.
8 You don't have to pay to use the computers.
9 You have to bring a pen and some paper to lessons.
10 You don't have to bring a dictionary.

5

1 is going to do 2 aren't going to buy 3 is going to buy
4 's going to get 5 're going to have 6 isn't going to get
7 'm going to buy 8 Are you going to stay 9 Are you going to visit

6

1 Jo uses her phone to send emails.
2 Christine went to the supermarket to buy some eggs.
3 I use my iPod to listen to music.
4 Ali joined a club to meet new people.
5 I went to the park to meet my friends.

7

1 'd like 2 playing, to be 3 gardening, wouldn't like 4 listening
5 come 6 doesn't 7 to get 8 going, doesn't

8

1 download 2 primary 3 tutor 4 forum 5 talent 6 licence 7 charity

9

2 g 3 d 4 c 5 a 6 h 7 f 8 e

Pearson Education Limited
Edinburgh Gate
Harlow
Essex CM20 2JE
England
and Associated Companies throughout the world.

www.pearsonelt.com

First published 2011
Twelfth impression 2018

ISBNs:
9781408267332
New Total English Elementary Workbook with Key and Audio CD Pack
9781408267349
New Total English Elementary Workbook without Key and Audio CD Pack

Set in MetaPlusBook-Roman
Printed in Italy by L.E.G.O. S.p.A.

Design: Pearson Education

Photo acknowledgements

The publisher would like to thank the following for their kind permission to reproduce their photographs:

(Key: b-bottom; c-centre; l-left; r-right; t-top)

Alamy Images: Charlotte Wiig 52tr
Getty Images: 4tr, 48cl, Daniel Allan 72tl, Koichi Kamoshida 30cl;
iStockphoto: 5cr, 10tl, 16tr, 24tl, 32bc, 45br
Pearson Education Ltd: Chris Coggins 32bl, Gareth Boden 7cr, Image Source Ltd 8tc, 8c, 60tl, Jules Selmes 38tl, 65c, Mark Bassett 16tc, New Holland 8tl, Photodisc 27bl, 39bl, 63cr
Rex Features: David Fisher 5, Karl Schoendorfer 5tc, Sipa Press 68tr
Shutterstock.com: Ben Smith 5cl
Thinkstock: 7c (Below), 7cl, 7cl (Above), 7cl (Below), 9tr, 17cr, 26tr, 26cl, 26cr, 30bl, 32c, 32c (Below), 32cl, 32cl (Below), 39br, 56tr, 56c, 65tc, 65c (Below), 65cl (Above), BananaStock 8tr, Comstock 8cl, Digital Vision 70tr, Getty Images 25cr, Hemera Technologies 7c, Jack Hollingsworth 6tr, Jupiterimages 10tc, 11bl, 16tl, 20cl, 25tr, 65cl, 78r, Ryan McVay 12cl, Medioimages / Photodisc 65tl, Stockbyte 8cr

Cover images: *Front:* **Alamy Images:** GYRO Photography / amana images

All other images © Pearson Education

Picture research by Andrea Duffy

Every effort has been made to trace the copyright holders and we apologise in advance for any unintentional omissions. We would be pleased to insert the appropriate acknowledgement in any subsequent edition of this publication.